AIDS – It's not over yet

ISSUES FOR THE NINETIES

Volume 10

Editor

Craig Donnellan

Independence
Educational Publishers

First published by Independence
PO Box 295
Cambridge CB1 3XP

British Library Cataloguing in Publication Data
AIDS – It's not over yet – (Issues for the Nineties Series)
I. Donnellan, Craig II. Series
362.1969792

ISBN 1 872995 78 0

Printed in Great Britain
at Leicester Printers Ltd
Leicester

Typeset by
Martyn Lusher Artwork, Cambridge

Cover
The illustration on the front cover is by
Katherine Fleming / Folio Collective.

CONTENTS

Introduction

AIDS – It's not over yet is the tenth volume in the series: **Issues For The Nineties**. The aim of this series is to offer up-to-date information about important issues in our world.

AIDS – It's not over yet looks at the current situation, the effects of HIV and AIDS and seeking help. The information comes from a wide variety of sources and includes:

Government reports and statistics
Newspaper reports and features
Magazine articles and surveys
Literature from lobby groups
and charitable organisations.

It is hoped that, as you read about the many aspects of the issues explored in this book, you will critically evaluate the information presented. It is important that you decide whether you are being presented with facts or opinions. Does the writer give a biased or an unbiased report? If an opinion is being expressed, do you agree with the writer?

AIDS – It's not over yet offers a useful starting-point for those who need convenient access to information about the many issues involved. However, it is only a starting-point. At the back of the book is a list of organisations which you may want to contact for further information.

*****

Understanding HIV infection and AIDS

What is AIDS?

AIDS stands for Acquired Immune Deficiency Syndrome.

Acquired: it is a condition that can be acquired, to distinguish it from some similar conditions that some people are born with.

Immune: concerns the body's defence mechanism – the immune system.

Deficiency: concerns damage to the immune system.

Syndrome: a set of diseases or symptoms.

AIDS is therefore a condition in which progressive damage to the immune system has led to the development of certain illnesses.

AIDS first came to light in the USA in 1981 when the Centers for Disease Control (CDC), which monitor health data from local health departments, noticed a marked increase in a number of unusual infections, particularly amongst gay men. Until then these infections had only really been seen in people whose natural defences had been damaged by cancer or by drugs which suppress the immune system.

Doctors soon discovered that these men did indeed have an underlying deficiency of their immune system, but they had no idea what was causing it.

The condition was named Acquired Immune Deficiency Syndrome and, as more cases emerged from the USA, Europe and Africa, it became apparent that it was not confined to gay men.

What causes AIDS?

In 1983, more than a year after AIDS had been defined, a breakthrough was made in understanding its cause

and the virus that leads to AIDS was identified. This virus is known as HIV (the human immunodeficiency virus) and its action in the body is still being researched. It attacks the very cells in the body whose job it is to fight off infection – the cells of the immune system. In particular, HIV attacks a type of white blood cell known as the T-helper (or CD4) cell. These have a key role in the body's defence mechanisms by mobilising the elements of the immune system which attack and destroy germs (foreign bodies such as bacteria, viruses, fungi and protozoa).

HIV also infects other types of cell, including other blood cells and cells of the central nervous system.

Other theories about causes of AIDS

It is believed by some scientists and others that HIV does not cause immune suppression and AIDS by itself, but that other factors such as another virus may be involved.

Quite distinct from this view is the belief that HIV does not cause AIDS at all, but that the immune suppression which leads to AIDS is caused by sexual or drug lifestyle, poor diet or blood transfusions. This is a decidedly minority view and goes against the majority of scientific opinion.

How is HIV transmitted?

When AIDS was first identified in the USA, all those affected seemed to be gay or bisexual men. But it soon became apparent that other people were also affected including injecting drug users, people with haemophilia, people who had received blood transfusions, as well as heterosexuals who came into none of these categories.

Furthermore, it was discovered that while anyone can become infected with HIV, the ways in which this can happen are limited and the transfer of infected body fluids is always involved.

HIV is found in the blood and semen or vaginal fluid of a person with HIV or AIDS. An infected person can only infect someone else if the virus within these fluids enters the bloodstream of the other person. This can happen in four ways:

Unprotected sex
Where the penis enters the vagina or anus without a condom being used. Penetrative sex without a condom between men and women or men and men can lead to transmission of HIV if one partner is infected. The presence of other sexually transmitted diseases, such as genital ulcers, may increase the possibility of transmission. Oral sex has a far lower risk of transmission, though exactly how risky it is continues to be the subject of research and controversy.

Infected blood and blood products
HIV transmission via this route has now been virtually eliminated in industrialised countries through routine screening (testing) of donated blood. Most developing countries are now also improving their screening of blood for HIV

Re-use of needles or syringes
Can lead to the exchange of small quantities of blood, leading to transmission of the virus from one

person to the next. Injecting drug users who share 'works' can transmit the virus in this way. Re-using needles in a medical setting, which still occurs in some developing countries, could also lead to transmission.

From mother to child
(perinatal transmission)
Estimates are that in industrialised parts of the world such as Europe, around 1 in 7 of children born to mothers with HIV will themselves be infected. However, in other parts of the world this can rise to 1 in 3. Infection is also possible via breast milk, and in countries where there are safe alternatives women are advised not to breast-feed.

Preventing transmission of HIV

The Terrence Higgins Trust booklet *Preventing HIV Infection* describes safer sex and safer drug use. Briefly, they are:

Safer sex: adapting sex so that it is still enjoyable while transmission risk is kept to a minimum.

Safer drug use: never sharing drug-injecting equipment. Or, if it is impossible to avoid sharing, cleaning equipment between users.

In healthcare settings and when giving first aid there are various routine hygiene precautions which should always be followed. These prevent the transmission of HIV (and other more infectious viruses).

Where did HIV come from?

Many theories have been put forward as to the origin of AIDS but there is no scientific agreement. HIV may have been present for centuries in a relatively harmless form and only recently evolved into a more damaging one.

Origins remain of scientific interest but the important thing is:

AIDS is likely to be part of our world for

several decades – even if a cure or vaccine can be developed

There are positive steps – personal, social, national and international – which can and must be taken to prevent further spread of the virus and to care for the people already infected.

Some basic facts about HIV and AIDS

People can find out if they have HIV through a blood test that determines whether they have developed antibodies to HIV. Antibodies are part of the body's natural defences against germs such as viruses. Those who have antibodies for HIV are described as HIV antibody positive – or more simply, HIV positive.

People may not be aware that they are infected. The reported number of people known to have HIV only includes those who have taken a blood test, and is therefore only a proportion of the total number infected.

Most people with HIV remain perfectly healthy for several years. It is not yet known whether everyone with HIV will eventually become ill.

The strain of HIV with which someone is infected, their age and their general health all seem to affect the length of time it may take before

they develop AIDS. For many people it will be over 10 years.

Once infected, people remain infectious all their lives and can pass the virus on to others.

HIV is not contagious – it cannot be passed on by ordinary social contact in the same way as colds and flu are. It is not even as infectious as some other blood-borne viruses such as hepatitis B.

In a short time, HIV has become the most studied virus in history. Groups of scientists and clinicians are working to find out how it operates and to develop vaccines and a cure.

No vaccine is yet available. Although much research is underway throughout the world, it is unlikely that any effective vaccine will be widely available for another 10 years at the earliest. HIV changes its structure very easily and different strains can be found in one individual, making vaccine development difficult.

Although there is no cure for HIV doctors are becoming increasingly skilled at preventing and treating the various infections to which a person with a damaged immune system is vulnerable. Having AIDS does not necessarily mean constant sickness. The course of HIV infection varies considerably between individuals, so many people with AIDS continue to fight disease and live full lives.

The course of the infection

Being HIV positive is not the same as having AIDS.

Initial infection with HIV may be accompanied by mild flu-like symptoms. This is followed by a period in which the infected person feels quite well, although the virus continues to attack the T-helper cells which form a very important part of the immune system. This period can last many years. Eventually the number of T-helper cells declines and the virus multiplies. The

AIDS related infections

Several years may pass during which HIV decimates the white blood cells, the body's defensive immune system. As they are destroyed, AIDS-related infections take hold and account for 90 per cent of the deaths from AIDS

■ 7 – 8 years after infection
60–75 per cent of the white cells are destroyed. The first infections to appear are bacterial skin infections, thrush (painful sores of the mouth) and shingles (an infection of the nerves and skin).

Victims also suffer chronic fevers, diarrhoea, severe athlete's foot, night sweats and weight loss

■ 8 – 9 years after infection
75–95 per cent of the white cells are destroyed. Brain diseases such as menigitis and toxoplasmosis

Pneumonia and tubercolosis

■ 9 – 10 years
Herpes simplex infections to the skin, mucous membranes and oesophagus

Cytomegalovirus infection of the colon causes uncontrollable bleeding

Ulcers around genitals and rectum

SOURCES:
U.S. Center for Disease Control,
Scientific American,
Fairfield Hospital,
Melbourne, Australia

DUNCAN MIL
Graphic News

Death usually occurs by year 10

body becomes vulnerable to infections and conditions that do not normally trouble those with a healthy immune system, and the person may experience fever and night sweats, for example.

The term 'AIDS' is used if a person with HIV develops one or more serious infections from a list compiled by the Centers for Disease Control (CDC) in the USA. An example is PCP, Pneumocystis carinii pneumonia, which would normally cause no trouble to those with a healthy immune function.

Someone with HIV might fall ill with an infection or condition not on the CDC list, and they might be very ill indeed, but they would not necessarily have AIDS. The term 'AIDS-related complex' or ARC is still used by some doctors for HIV-related illness which does not meet the AIDS definition. Now many people prefer to use the term 'HIV disease' when a person with HIV has any illness, because this avoids the impression of a 'hierarchy of illness' or inevitable decline.

Whatever it is called, the course of illness in people infected with HIV is variable, unpredictable and dependent on many factors. These include the psychological state of the individual, their previous state of health and their access to a decent standard of living, such as adequate diet and warm, dry housing.

HIV and AIDS worldwide

The World Health Organisation (WHO) estimates that 18 million adults and 1.5 million children have been infected by HIV since the start of the worldwide epidemic. Half of all new infections are believed to occur in people under 25.

By the year 2000, it is possible that 30 to 40 million men, women and children will have been infected by HIV. Over ninety per cent of these infections are likely to have occurred in developing countries, primarily through heterosexual intercourse.

The total number of people estimated to have developed AIDS reached 4.5 million at the end of 1994 and could rise to 10 million by the year 2000. Today the majority of reported cases are concentrated in Africa, Europe and the Americas, but AIDS is also claiming increasing numbers of lives in Asia.

The overall world picture shows:
- The basic modes of transmission have not changed.
- There is a highly variable distribution of HIV infection.
- The epidemic is dynamic, unstable and continuing to spread rapidly.

Source: World Health Organisation

The international response

AIDS has challenged the notion that medical science can conquer all disease. The achievements of modern medicine – transplants, cancer therapies, test-tube babies – pale before this new worldwide threat to human health.

In the absence of a vaccine or cure, only preventative and educational measures will halt the spread of HIV. Although the WHO has called for a worldwide effort to stop AIDS, responses to the epidemic have varied considerably from country to country. As the former Director of the WHO Global Programme on AIDS has said: 'Denial at personal, social, national and international level has been a constant problem and remains today a grave threat to public health.'

Because AIDS was initially seen to be confined to particular groups, some countries which associated drug-taking and homosexuality with deviant or criminal behaviour took punitive measures.

Several countries refuse entry to people who are HIV positive or who have AIDS. The USA, for example, imposes restrictions on visitors with HIV. Others, such as Bulgaria and Cuba, have tested all their citizens for HIV. Cuba has isolated people who turned out to be HIV positive. Apart from the ethical questions, the costs of these measures are disproportionate to any public health benefits. Results have shown very low levels of infection amongst the general population, as was to be expected.

The World Health Organisation has recommended that there is no ethical or public health basis for mass testing. This is a view endorsed by most countries.

- The above is an extract from *Understanding HIV Infection and AIDS*, published by The Terrence Higgins Trust. See page 39 for address details.

© The Terrence Higgins Trust
May, 1995

HIV/AIDS: a chronology

1981 AIDS first recognised in gay men in the US

1982 Blood transmission detected; AIDS recognised in Zaire in heterosexuals

1983 HIV-1 first isolated (under the name LAV in France, later as HTLV-III in the US; renamed HIV in 1986)

1984 HIV confirmed as cause of AIDS; first antibody tests

1986 First trials of AZT in AIDS patients; HIV-2 found in West Africa

1987 AZT licensed for treating AIDS

1989 Monkey experiments show vaccines based on SIV can protect animals from infection

1990 AZT approved for treating symptom-free people with HIV

1992 AIDS deaths top 500,000; dramatic results reported for vaccines based on live, altered virus with genes deleted

1993 Concorde trials shows AZT cannot delay AIDS

1994 Early trials show AZT can cut risk of mother-child transmission by two-thirds. AIDS cases rise 60%, WHO estimates 4 million have the disease and 17 million people have been infected with HIV

© WorldAIDS
January, 1995

Social trends

From the Office of Population Censuses and Surveys

The Human Immunodeficiency Virus (HIV) is the virus which causes AIDS (Acquired Immune Deficiency Syndrome). However, there can be a long period between infection with the virus and the onset of AIDS. It is estimated that ten years after infection about 50 per cent of people will have developed AIDS. In 1993 it is estimated that 2.1 thousand new AIDS cases will have been diagnosed in England and Wales (Chart 1). Sex between men still predominates as the main exposure category. However, sex between men and women accounted for nearly one in five of these cases in 1993 compared with only around one in nine in 1990.

The long incubation period of HIV means that these AIDS figures reflect patterns of transmission several years ago. A more accurate picture of current transmission is given by the anonymised HIV surveys. Data to the end of June 1993 indicate that in the ante natal clinics being surveyed in London, prevalence among attenders has risen from 1 in 500 in 1990 to 1 in 380 in the first six months of 1993, while prevalence outside London has remained at over 1 in 9 over the same period. Comparison of these results with the number of births to HIV-infected women reported indicates that the majority of infections in pregnant women had not been diagnosed. In 1992 the Department of Health issued guidance to health authorities encouraging ante natal clinics in higher-risk areas to offer HIV testing to pregnant women. This was reissued with minor revisions in June 1994.

By September 1994, a cumulative total of 9.9 thousand AIDS cases had been reported and 6.7 thousand deaths from AIDS were known to have occurred in the United Kingdom; females accounted for only 8 per cent of cases and 7 per cent of deaths.

In 1993 there were 1.6 thousand AIDS cases reported in the United Kingdom, a rate of 2.8 per 100 thousand population. Chart 2 compares the number of AIDS cases reported in 1993 in the various countries of the European Community (EC), expressed as a rate per 100 thousand population. Spain has the highest rate at 9.9. The United Kingdom had one of the lowest rates in the EC; only Greece, the Irish Republic and Belgium had lower rates. *Source: Social Trends 25*
© *Crown copyright, 1995*

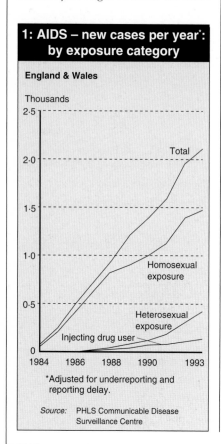

1: AIDS – new cases per year*: by exposure category

England & Wales

Thousands

*Adjusted for underreporting and reporting delay.

Source: PHLS Communicable Disease Surveillance Centre

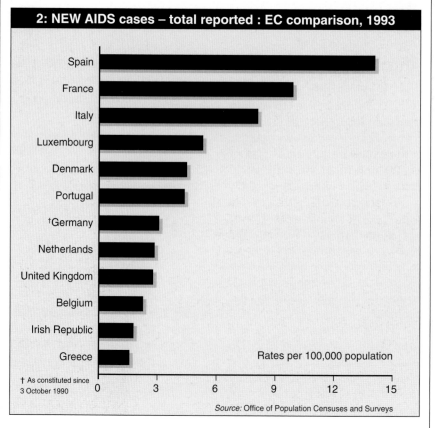

2: NEW AIDS cases – total reported : EC comparison, 1993

Spain
France
Italy
Luxembourg
Denmark
Portugal
†Germany
Netherlands
United Kingdom
Belgium
Irish Republic
Greece

Rates per 100,000 population

† As constituted since 3 October 1990

Source: Office of Population Censuses and Surveys

AIDS cases and incidence rates per million population* by country and year of diagnosis† reported by 30 June 1995 WHO European Region

Country	1992 N	1992 Rate	1993 N	1993 Rate	1994 N	1994 Rate	Jan-June 95 N	Cumulative Total
Albania	0	0.0	0	0.0	0	0.0	0	0
Austria	186	23.8	223	28.4	161	20.3	81	1408
Azerbaijan	0	0.0	0	0.0	1	0.1	0	1
Belarus	5	0.5	2	0.2	2	0.2	1	13
Belgium	245	24.5	251	25.0	254	25.2	163	2053
Bulgaria	6	0.7	6	0.7	10	1.1	1	35
Croatia	8	1.8	10	2.2	17	3.8	8	85
Czech Rep.	9	0.9	15	1.5	12	1.2	8	67
Denmark	208	40.3	242	46.9	242	46.8	133	1775
Estonia	2	1.3	1	0.6	1	0.6	0	4
Finland	20	4.0	25	4.9	47	9.2	22	217
France	5088	86.5	5513	93.3	5839	98.4	2705	39310
Germany	1735	21.6	1831	22.6	1869	23.0	818	14260
Greece	169	16.4	184	17.7	164	15.7	93	1164
Hungary	33	.32	33	3.2	23	2.3	13	184
Iceland	3	11.5	6	22.8	3	11.3	0	35
Ireland	71	20.2	73	20.7	66	18.6	14	503
Israel	34	6.8	50	9.5	30	5.5	26	346
Italy	4237	74.2	4850	84.9	5733	100.3	3179	30900
Kazakhstan	0	0.0	2	0.1	3	0.2	0	5
Latvia	1	0.4	3	1.1	2	0.8	0	9
Lithuania	1	0.3	1	0.3	0	0.0	1	6
Luxembourg	12	30.8	20	50.6	13	32.4	7	97
Malta	4	11.1	3	8.3	5	13.7	1	35
Moldova Rep.	2	0.5	0	0.0	0	0.0	1	5
Monaco	9	290.3	7	225.8	3	96.8	2	35
Netherlands	507	33.4	463	30.3	456	29.6	230	3734
Norway	51	11.9	64	14.9	71	16.9	22	470
Poland	35	0.9	69	1.8	103	2.7	37	340
Portugal	392	39.8	540	54.9	672	68.4	282	2947
Romania	435	18.8	432	18.8	485	21.2	313	3535
Russian Fed.	29	0.2	13	0.1	32	0.2	23	198
San Marino	0	0.0	0	0.0	0	0.0	0	1
Slovak Rep.	3	0.6	1	0.2	3	0.6	2	12
Slovenia	3	1.6	7	3.6	6	3.1	6	43
Spain	4812	122.0	5427	137.3	7557	1910	3909	37073
Sweden	130	15.0	181	20.8	183	20.9	82	1254
Switzerland	726	104.0	676	95.8	699	98.0	394	5324
Tajikistan	0	0.0	0	0.0	0	0.0	0	0
Turkey	30	0.5	35	0.6	40	0.7	13	186
Ukraine	4	0.1	10	0.2	10	0.2	8	40
United Kingdom	1516	26.2	1660	28.7	1687	29.0	688	11641
Uzbokistan	1	0.0	1	0.0	0	0.0	0	2
Yugoslavia, F.R.§	90	8.6	72	6.8	9.	8.4	64	507
Total	**20852**		**23002**		**26596**		**13350**	**159859**

* Source of population data: World Population Prospects: The 1994 Revision (United Nations, New York)
† Data adjusted for reporting delay (time between AIDS diagnosis and report)
§ Serbia & Montenegro

From European Centre for the Epidemiological Monitoring of AIDS, HIV/AIDS Surveillance in Europe, Quarterly Report n° 46, 30 June 1995, page 13

Global statistics – AIDS

From CAB International

By the end of 1994 the World Health Organisation had received reports of a cumulative total of 1,025,073 cases of AIDS in adults and children throughout the world. The total represents a 20% increase on the 851,628 cases reported by the end of 1993. The regional totals are as follows:

Region	No. of cases
Africa	347,713
Americas	526,682
Asia	17,057
Europe	127,886
Oceania	5,735

The greatest proportionate increase was seen in Asia, where the number of reported cases has nearly doubled since the end of June 1994 (when 8,968 cases were recorded), most in Thailand where 13,246 cases had been recorded by late October. India acknowledged 885 cases by late November (compare the 832 known in Japan). The WHO estimates that the actual number of cases since the beginning of the epidemic is more than 4.5 million. Of the known cases 39% were recorded in the USA, 34% in Africa, 12.5% in Europe and 12% in the rest of the Americas; only 2% were in Asia. With regard to the estimated total, the WHO reckons that more than 70% have been in Africa, more than 9% in the Americas outside the USA and 9% in the USA itself, about 6% in Asia and 4% in Europe.

In Africa substantial increases compared with the June 1994 figures were recorded in Chad (2,341 cases, previously 1,523), Eritrea (1,193 cases compared with 372 known by the end of 1992), Malawi (34,167, an increase of some 2,300 in six months), Senegal (1,297, compared with 911 in mid-1993), South Africa (3,849, up 640 in five months), Zaire

(26,131, three months after the previous report of 22,747 in late April 1994 [although the accuracy of these figures must be doubted, as an underestimate, given the parlous conditions in the country and the influx of refugees from Rwanda and now Burundi – Eds]) and Zimbabwe (33,063 compared with 27,905 eleven months earlier).

Elsewhere, Brazil reported 55,894 cases, an increase of 6,500 in six months, and the USA 401,789 (by late September 1994). France has the highest recorded number in Europe (32,722 by the end of September compared with 27,584 in Spain and 24,511 by the same time in Italy). The Maldives reported a case for the first time. Montserrat reduced its total by one to 6.

Weekly Epidemiological Record, 1995, 70(2), 5-8

Global estimates of HIV

The World Health Organisation estimates that since the beginning of the epidemic some 18 million adults and about 1.5 million children had been infected with HIV by late 1994. It has also estimated the global distribution of total adult infections and of adults alive by the end of 1994; see the table below.

The number of infected adults alive is put at between 13 and 15 million, and the continuing increase, particularly in Southern and Central Africa and South Asia, will accentuate the disproportionate impact of HIV/AIDS on the developing world.

Weekly Epidemiological Record, 1995, 70(2), 7-8

● The above is an extract from *AIDS News*, March 1995, Vol. 10, produced by CAB International.

© *CAB International*

Global estimates of HIV – 1995

Region	Adult infections	Adults alive
North America	>1,000,000	>750,000
Latin America and the Caribbean	2,000,000	<1,500,000
Sub-Saharan Africa	11,000,000	> 8,000,000
North Africa and the Middle East	>100,000	>100,000
Western Europe	>500,000	450,000
Eastern Europe and Central Asia	>50,000	>50,000
East Asia and the Pacific	>50,000	50,000
South and South-east Asia	3,000,000	>2,500,000
Australasia	>25,000	>20,000

Some myths dispelled

Understanding HIV infection and AIDS

Can I contract HIV from meeting an infected person?
Having a friend, acquaintance, work colleague or partner with HIV is perfectly safe, unless you have certain types of sex with them or share drug-injecting equipment with them. More than ten years into the epidemic, there is no evidence to suggest that the virus can pass between two people in any other way. If it could live in or travel through air like cold or flu viruses, a completely different pattern of infection would have emerged.

Can HIV be transmitted by sharing a cup or glass with someone who is infected?
No. The Centers for Disease Control in the USA have looked at the families of HIV-positive people who were sharing facilities such as toilets, baths, beds, crockery and cutlery. Apart from sexual partners and children born to infected mothers, not one person out of more than 12,000 people studied became infected.

Can mosquitoes spread HIV?
Mosquitoes cannot transmit HIV to people (and the same applies to lice, fleas, ticks and bed bugs). This is clear from the pattern of infection in countries with high numbers of mosquitoes. In Africa, for example, it was recognised early on that infected people were either sexually active adults or babies born to adults with the virus.

The Terrence Higgins Trust

Can HIV live in swimming pools?
No, the standard water treatment is sufficient to kill HIV. Also, the water would dilute the virus to such an extent that even if it was not killed, there would be no risk of anyone becoming infected. HIV cannot be transmitted in this way.

Can HIV live on damp towels or lavatory seats?
Laboratory tests have shown that HIV may survive in dried blood for 5 or 6 days. However, in order for someone to become infected, sufficient quantity of the virus would need to enter their bloodstream. In the last 10 years, thousands of infected and uninfected people have lived and worked together, and no new unexplained infections have occurred. HIV cannot be transmitted in this way.

What is the risk of HIV transmission while giving first aid to an accident casualty?
The risk is very small. It is always sensible to avoid contact with blood spillages as much as possible when giving first aid to anyone. There is a theoretical risk of transmission of HIV or other blood-borne infections if the casualty is bleeding and the first aider gets blood on a graze, in an eye or in their mouth. No cases of HIV infection have occurred as a result of mouth-to-mouth resuscitation.

Is there any risk from giving blood?
In industrialised countries and any country where needles are not re-used, there is absolutely no possibility of becoming infected with HIV by being a blood donor. Furthermore, all donated blood is tested for antibodies to HIV and other blood-borne infections before it is used.

● The above is an extract from *Understanding HIV infection and AIDS*, produced by The Terrence Higgins Trust. See page 39 for address details.

Cumulative infections approach 20 million

From Global AIDSnews

Around 2.5 million people were newly infected in 1994 with the human immunodeficiency virus, according to Global Programme on AIDS (GPA) estimates published in January. This took the total number of people infected with HIV to 19.5 million, including 1.5 million children, since the start of the pandemic.

Sub-Saharan Africa, where the cumulative number of infections among adults rose an estimated 11 million, remained hardest hit by the pandemic. But proportionately the greatest increase by region was in South and South-East Asia, where the total of HIV infections among adults rose to three million in 1994 from two million at the end of 1993.

The number of people estimated to have developed AIDS since the start of the pandemic rose to around 4.5 million at the end of 1994. This is more than four times the figure actually reported to GPA, which rose by 20% to 1,025,073 in the 12 months to 31 December 1994. The difference between the estimated and reported figures is due to under-reporting and statistical delays.

The new estimated total of cumulative HIV infections in sub-Saharan Africa includes a recent upward adjustment of incidence in the region since the start of the pandemic. The figures are therefore not directly comparable with previous data published in Global AIDSnews.

Note: Articles and illustrations published in Global AIDSnews which are not copyright may be reproduced provided credit is given to WHO/GPA and provided such reproduction is not used for commercial purposes. Signed articles do not necessarily reflect the views of WHO.
© WHO (GPA) 1995

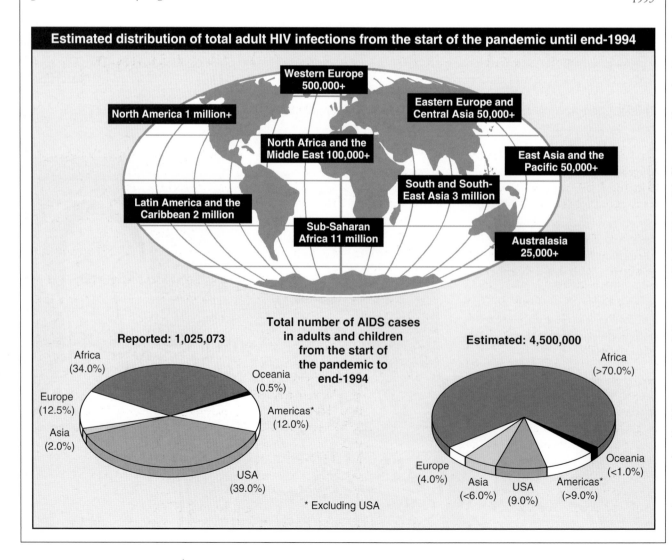

Estimated distribution of total adult HIV infections from the start of the pandemic until end-1994

Western Europe 500,000+

North America 1 million+

Eastern Europe and Central Asia 50,000+

North Africa and the Middle East 100,000+

East Asia and the Pacific 50,000+

Latin America and the Caribbean 2 million

South and South-East Asia 3 million

Sub-Saharan Africa 11 million

Australasia 25,000+

Total number of AIDS cases in adults and children from the start of the pandemic to end-1994

Reported: 1,025,073
- Africa (34.0%)
- Europe (12.5%)
- Asia (2.0%)
- USA (39.0%)
- Americas* (12.0%)
- Oceania (0.5%)

Estimated: 4,500,000
- Africa (>70.0%)
- Europe (4.0%)
- Asia (<6.0%)
- USA (9.0%)
- Americas* (>9.0%)
- Oceania (<1.0%)

* Excluding USA

8

Aids cases total passes 10,000

By David Brindle
Social Services Correspondent

The number of Aids cases in Britain has passed 10,000, according to official figures released yesterday which show new cases rising at an annual rate of 11 per cent.

Registered cases of HIV infection, which can lead to Aids, have reached more than 23,000. Twenty-eight per cent of people newly infected are acquiring the virus through heterosexual sex.

Although the spread of Aids is far slower than was previously feared, these figures show that cases are occurring at rate of almost five a day.

The total number of people in the United Kingdom who have contracted Aids rose 442 to 10,304 in the last quarter of 1994. Counting began in 1982. Of the total, 890 (8.6 per cent) have been women, and 7,019 (68 per cent) have died.

There were 1,789 new cases notified during 1994, 11 per cent up on the 1993 figure of 1,609. The overwhelming majority of Aids cases continues to come from the Thames health regions, covering London. However, there have been 3,044 in the rest of England, 604 in Scotland, 141 in Wales, and 49 in N. Ireland.

Among new cases, the rate of increase is faster in the rest of England and in Wales than in the Thames regions and Scotland. The total of notified HIV cases in the UK had reached 23,104 by the end of last month, of which 3,201 (13.9 per cent) were women. Counting began in 1984.

Of the 2,411 new cases last year, 56 per cent were attributed to sex between men, compared to 60 per cent of all cases since monitoring started. Heterosexual sex was the cause in 28 per cent of new cases, compared to 17 per cent of all.

The virus was passed to a baby from its parents in 43 cases last year and in 280 of all cases since 1982 – the carrier having been the mother in exactly half.

© The Guardian
January, 1995

News from the Americas

AIDS among women

In 1994, 18% of the 79,674 persons aged 13 years and older with AIDS in the USA were women. The corresponding figure in 1985 was 7% (534 of 8,153). Women aged 15-44 years accounted for 84% of cases with a median age of 35. Blacks and Hispanics accounted for 77% of reported cases among infected women.

The infection rate among Black and Hispanic women was 16 and 7 times higher, respectively, than those for white women. Infection was most prevalent in the Northeast region (44%) followed by the South (36%), West (9%), Midwest (7%) and Puerto Rico and US territories (4%). In the Northeast, women with AIDS mainly lived in urban areas whereas in the South 10.2% (compared with 1.4% in the Northeast) lived outside the metropolitan areas. Some 61% of all cases were reported from 5 states: New York (26%); Florida (13%); New Jersey (10%); California (7%); and Texas (5%).

The main routes of infection were: injecting drug use (41%); heterosexual contact with a partner at risk for or known to have HIV infection or AIDS (38%); and receipt of contaminated blood or blood products (2%).

Some 19% who initially reported no specific HIV exposure were later reclassified. Most had heterosexual contact with an at-risk partner (66%) or a history of drug abuse (27%). The HIV Survey of Childbearing Women showed that an estimated 7,000 HIV-infected women delivered babies in the USA during 1993. An assumed perinatal trans-mission rate of 15-30% means that between 1,000 and 2,000 infants were perinatally infected with HIV during 1993.

Between 1989 and 1993 the annual prevalence of HIV infection among childbearing women remained fairly constant (1.6-1.7/1000), although regional variations were evident: in the Northeast, prevalence decreased from 4.1 to 3.4/1000; in the South, it increased from 1.6 in 1989 to 2.0 in 1991 and remained constant in 1993.

Morbidity and Mortality Weekly Report
1995, 44(5), 81-84

● The above is an extract from *AIDS News*, March 1995, Vol. 10, produced by CAB International.

African villages cut HIV by 42pc

Tim Radford on a high yield experiment

In the first major experiment of its kind, European and African scientists have shown the spread of HIV infection in Africa can be slowed

They have confirmed – in the *Lancet* today – that other sexually transmitted diseases increase the spread of Aids.

The two-year, £2 million study, shows that transmission of the virus could be cut by almost 50 per cent by intensive treatment of other sexually transmitted diseases.

This in a continent where 90 per cent of all HIV infection is heterosexual and where infection rates in the cities have reached 20 per cent.

The research has involved the Tanzanian Government, medical charities, and the London School of Hygiene and Tropical Medicine, and the co-operation of thousands of villagers in Mwanza, Tanzania.

According to David Mabey and Richard Hayes, of the London School, Aids scientists have long suspected the spread of HIV infection would be helped by other venereal diseases such as syphilis and gonorrhoea.

With the help of the African medical services, and money from Europe, the researchers selected 12 village health centres on or near Lake Victoria, where HIV was spreading at roughly 1 per cent per year, and divided them into two groups, matching them as closely as possible for site and population.

In one of each matched pair they invested new training for health workers, an education programme, and a proper supply of drugs of the kind permitted by the Tanzanian economy. In the other village, things were left to proceed as normal.

In Africa 90 per cent of all HIV infection is heterosexual and infection rates in the cities have reached 20 per cent

---

The results – even before the examination of HIV transmission – were dramatic. More people with symptoms came to clinics, more of them were diagnosed correctly and treated successfully first time, and the remainder were referred for more specialist treatment. At relatively little cost, the village health centres cured around 99 per cent of all sexually transmitted diseases brought to them.

Two years later – by which time better health services were also being introduced into the 'control' villages – doctors began to test the difference in rates of HIV infection in groups of 1,000 people in all 12 villages The result was stark: the extra training, and the regular supply of drugs, had reduced HIV transmission in the six villages by 42 per cent.

The effect was not only on a village-by-village level, it was also the same for all ages and both sexes in each group tested. Professor Mabey said: 'Now we have a study which has shown, I think clearly, that a relatively simple intervention in one of the world's poorest countries has managed to have a very substantial impact and I think now there is no excuse for donor agencies to withhold their resources.'

© *The Guardian*
August, 1995

Photo: Jacky Chapman / Format

The extra training, and the regular supply of drugs, had reduced HIV transmission in the six villages by 42 per cent

Africa is priority for new UN AIDS chief

By Emilia Casella

Africa will be the top priority under the United Nations' new AIDS programme – reversing a trend which has drawn international attention away from the embattled continent, vows its director, Belgian Dr Peter Piot.

Piot told *WorldAIDS* in January that the climate among UN donor countries is that African programmes 'have not given the results hoped for. I will definitely fight against that.

'Africa will still be the highest on the agenda, not only because the epidemic is most severe there, but also because I believe that in most Asian countries there is a stronger capacity to respond to the problem,' compared to some African countries which need more direct support, said Piot.

Piot was appointed in December to head the UN's new Joint Co-Sponsored Programme on HIV and AIDS, a complete overhaul of the UN's approach to AIDS which will merge the AIDS programmes of five UN agencies plus the World Bank. It is to begin operation in January 1996.

The new programme will change the way the UN spends money on AIDS with an initial budget of about US$90 million, equivalent to the current budget of WHO's Global Programme on AIDS, which will cease operation by the end of 1995 – and is likely to affect the way individual countries approach the disease.

However, with less than a year until its launch, much is still not known about how the mega-agency will work. While some AIDS workers have heard vague rumblings about it, most of those who will be most affected – people with AIDS – have not.

A transition team in Geneva was to have produced a draft mission statement by the end of January mapping out the programme's mandate, budget and operational structure.

The team's work sparked criticism that the UN has put the cart before the horses by developing the organisation before determining its strategy.

'I agree with that, but that is the process I inherited … it's definitely a handicap,' admitted Piot, adding he will conduct a wide strategy consultation in the first part of this year with non-government organisations (NGOs), country representatives and AIDS workers. Coordination is also expected at country level.

Piot says the UN must begin focusing on the social and economic aspects of the pandemic – not just its medical implications.

'In the 14 years we've known of AIDS, we've learned there's no single simplistic approach that will work. Although we've had some successes, they have been small-scale and not sustainable. If we do prevention without an environment that is supportive and sustainable, then we're really in trouble.'

But Dr Timothy Stamps, Zimbabwe's Minister of Health and Child Welfare, says that much of the new programme's success will depend on each country's health system, its budget and its relationship with UN officials on the ground.

He is also worried about political constraints: 'Ultimately, the policy-maker, however reluctant it claims to be, will be the World Bank. How much investment is the world prepared to put into an issue which, for many countries – even if they have HIV problems – is not a major issue and from the point of view of votes is not a consideration? Preventing blacks from getting AIDS in developing countries won't get many votes for a politician in the developed world.'

Dr Jonathan Mann, former head of GPA and now chair of the US-based Global AIDS Policy Coalition, is also concerned: 'If it does not develop a coherent strategic approach it will be less than – or at best, only equal to – the sum of its parts. So we will be no further along than where we are today.'

The six organisations involved in the merger are WHO, the UN Development Programme, the UN Population Fund, UNICEF, UNESCO and the World Bank. 'It's certainly true that working with six agencies is not going to be easy,' said Piot.

'I will be judged not by whether I got along with the agency heads, but whether there will be an impact at country level. What is needed here, definitely, is better coordination.'

© *WorldAIDS*
March, 1995

11

A toehold

Education has not stopped it. Nor has condom distribution. Indeed, none of the various efforts to slow the spread of HIV across sub-Saharan Africa has yet made a demonstrable difference. Hence the interest in a study, published in the August 26th issue of the *Lancet*, which shows that the transmission of the virus can be dramatically reduced through the treatment of other sexually transmitted diseases.

There is nothing new in the notion that the high prevalence of HIV infection among both men and women in Africa stems from the much higher prevalence of sexually transmitted diseases, particularly ones such as syphilis and chancroid that result in suppurating genital sores. But this is the first time that a controlled trial has shown that treatment can make a significant difference.

> **This is the first time that a controlled trial has shown that treatment can make a significant difference**

The researchers, who came from institutes in Tanzania, Britain and Holland, chose 12 villages in rural Tanzania, and, within each village, tested 1,000 adults for infection with HIV. Then, health workers from half of the villages were sent off to training programmes and supplied with better drugs for the treatment of four diseases: syphilis, chancroid, gonorrhoea and chlamydia. The remaining villages carried on as before. After two years, all the same adults were tested again. Adults from villages with improved health clinics were 42% less likely to test positive for HIV.

Unfortunately, implementing such programmes on a larger scale is not easy. Treatment is expensive. Gonorrhoea and chancroid are resistant to cheap antibiotics. The best drugs cost $10-15 for each treatment – too much for governments of poor countries. Syphilis, gonorrhoea and chlamydia do not produce symptoms in everybody. Many people will not even know they have a disease; many of those who do will not come for treatment anyway. Screening for the diseases in the population at large requires equipment and training.

One approach might be to forgo screening and just treat everyone. One such programme to treat the masses has just been started in Uganda, but whether it is successful will not be known for some years.

One danger of treating everyone is that if the drugs are not given in large enough doses, the diseases may become resistant to the new treatments. But in Africa it may be worth the risk – and it is probably easier than changing people's behaviour.

Only 4% of the adults in the rural Tanzanian study were HIV positive. Along main roads in Tanzania, that figure reaches 8%; in cities it is 11%. In some parts of southern Africa, the prevalence of HIV among women attending antenatal clinics may be as high as 25%. Although malaria kills more people in Africa, HIV kills people during their most productive years, destroying families and the workforce. This study has given hope at last that something can change.

© *The Economist*
26th August, 1995

Aids tide has turned in Europe, claims professor

By Victoria Macdonald
Health Correspondent

The multi-billion pound Aids industry is in turmoil over claims by the French scientist who discovered the HIV virus in 1983 that the disease has stabilised and is even declining in parts of northern Europe. Professor Luc Montagnier, president of the World Foundation of Aids Research and Prevention, has delivered a blow to patient organisations, saying that the problem is currently most severe in Africa and Asia and that efforts should now be concentrated there.

In an interview with The *Sunday Telegraph*, Prof. Montagnier said it was time the public was told the truth.

He said there was no 'explosion' of Aids in northern Europe, adding that it was wrong to frighten the general public into thinking that there was a high risk of catching the disease, because it only caused a backlash when it did not appear.

His statement was immediately condemned by the Paris branch of Act Up, the lobby group for homosexuals. A spokesman accused him of ignoring the plight of French Aids patients, some of whom, they say, are unable to receive treatment.

In England, Aids groups said that it was wrong of Prof. Montagnier to pit Europe against Africa when both areas had their own specific problems with the disease.

Prof. Montagnier said he regretted falling out with Aids patients' organisations but he believes he has the public's support. The dispute between Prof. Montagnier and the Aids organisations escalated following his resignation from ECS (translated as Everybody against Aids), an umbrella group of France's Aids organisations. Prof. Montagnier claims that ECS had refused to distribute money raised from a national telethon-type event to

African countries. 'They said they did not have enough,' Prof. Montagnier said.

Since his discovery in 1983 of the HIV virus, which can lead to Aids, Prof. Montagnier has worked to persuade governments and international organisations to take action against its spread.

In the UK, the number of people diagnosed with HIV was 2,766 in 1985. Last year, the number was 2,411, according to official figures. But Aids organisations here expressed disquiet over Prof. Montagnier's stand. Nick Partridge,

of the Terrence Higgins Trust, said it was wrong to pit the needs of people in Europe with Aids against those in Africa and Asia. 'We cannot let people run away with the idea that Aids in the UK is not having a significant impact,' Mr Partridge said. 'The achievement we have had in containing the epidemic here could be reversed if we let up on the campaigns now.'

Dr Patrick Dixon, founder of Aids Care Education and Training, which provides help to Aids patients here and abroad, said he believed Prof. Montagnier was showing signs of despondency that billions of dollars had been spent on the disease with no sign of a vaccine.

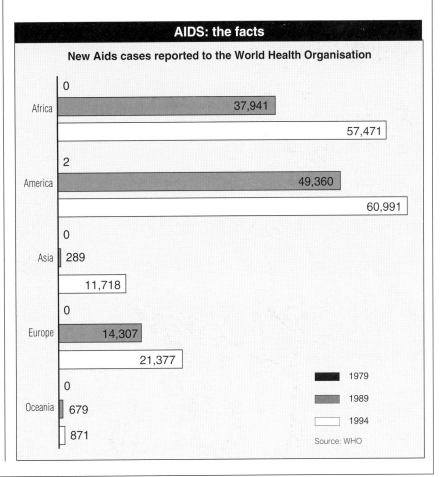

AIDS: the facts

New Aids cases reported to the World Health Organisation

Region	1979	1989	1994
Africa	0	37,941	57,471
America	2	49,360	60,991
Asia	0	289	11,718
Europe	0	14,307	21,377
Oceania	0	679	871

Source: WHO

Aids epidemic
'threatens booming economies'

By Nicholas Cumming-Bruce
Bangkok

Medical experts, academics and social workers from 60 countries meeting in the Thai city of Chiang Mai are debating measures to save Asia's booming economies from the threat of an Aids epidemic.

The Third International Conference on Aids in Asia comes as experts predict that the region will surpass Africa as the area most stricken by the disease by the end of the century. It already leads the world in new HIV infections, and by the year 2000 is expected to suffer more than the rest of the world put together. This would drain resources enough to undermine Asia's economic growth, analysts fear.

'Since... the end of 1992, the crisis that is the spread of HIV in Asia and the Pacific has tragically deepened,' John Dwyer, president of the Aids Society for Asia and the Pacific, said. 'Inexorably it appears as though the epicentre of the epidemic is moving from sub-Saharan Africa to Asia.'

He urged the region's governments to collaborate in fighting the disease. 'We are losing the fight,' he said.

Thai experts believe Thailand already accounts for 800,000 to a million of Asia's estimated 3 million HIV carriers. Although the rate of infection has stabilised, it is fuelling the spread of tuberculosis, increasing the strain on medical facilities.

India, however, is likely to become Asia's HIV capital, with 4 million cases by the turn of the century, according to United Nations Development Programme figures. Concern is mounting for smaller countries such as Cambodia, emerging from decades of war, which the World Health Organisation estimates is suffering the world's fastest rate of new infection.

Experts say the number of people in Asia with full-blown Aids has quadrupled to 2 million in the past two years, and will rise to 10 million by the end of the century. Most are young.

> **'Since the end of 1992, the spread of HIV in Asia and the Pacific has tragically deepened'**

One Thai academic says that Thailand, though enjoying some of the region's highest economic growth, stands to lose up to £6 billion in healthcare costs and lost production by the end of the century.

Mechai Viravaidya, a Thai birth control and anti-Aids campaigner, has warned the country will also lose up to £1.3 billion in tourism revenue a year.

Thailand has reached an agreement with China, which will help distribute and administer a herbal treatment said to slow the onset of Aids. The two countries will also co-operate in seeking a cure.

The HIV bandits no prison can hold

A gang of drug addicts who have robbed at least five Italian banks are immune from prosecution because they are HIV positive.

The law prohibits the jailing of people carrying the virus which can cause AIDS. Every time members of the four-man gang are arrested, police in Turin must release them.

Antonio Lamarra, 26, and Ferdinando Attanasio, 37, were back on the streets hours after being caught fleeing from a robbery last week.

The gang, armed with flick-knives, struck at another bank on Tuesday. Lamarra, Attanasio and two accomplices made off with £18,000.

Lamarra and Attanasio were arrested again yesterday and detained in a hospital. But police spokesman Filippo Dispenza said the authorities would have to release them after their court appearance. 'We are very worried about this,' he added.

A female drug addict who threatened a girl of five with a syringe in a Turin park before stealing her aunt's purse was released from custody this week after presenting a medical note saying she was HIV positive.

Government is wasting funds on Aids prevention

Official predictions of epidemic among heterosexuals were wrong, academics claim

The Government is wasting public money on programmes to prevent and control the spread of Aids in Scotland, according to two academics.

In a paper being published today, Barrie Craven a research fellow at the University of Northumbria, and Professor Gordon T. Stewart, former Emeritus Professor of Public Health at the University of Glasgow, say funding and staffing levels for Aids programmes are unjustifiable. They say other branches of medicine may be suffering.

Mr Craven, a right-wing economist, and Professor Stewart believe that Government predictions made ten years ago of a possible Aids epidemic in Britain were wrong. Subsequent claims by the Government that their public education programme has been highly successful are also misleading, they say.

Professor Stewart claims that Aids is costing the country about 250 million a year. 'It is a grotesque deception of the general public and quite indecent expenditure of public money.'

Mr Craven, who has previously argued that crime could be eradicated in Britain if criminals were executed or had limbs amputated, says the overwhelming majority of Aids cases involve homosexual or bisexual men, drug addicts and women who are their partners. 'The spread to the heterosexual population has not happened,' he says.

The paper, 'Corporate Governance, Financial Reporting, Regulation and the Aids Threat in Scotland', appears in the journal *Financial Accountability and Management*. It says there are more Aids workers in Britain than Aids

By Gillian Bowditch
Scotland Correspondent

patients and that Lothian Health Authority is spending £10.96 for every person, on Aids programmes.

Mr Craven believes that about 80 per cent of the expenditure on Aids in Scotland is unnecessary. 'The public has been unnecessarily alarmed by the Government's campaign.'

There are more Aids workers in Britain than Aids patients

Laurence Gruer, HIV and addictions co-ordinator for Greater Glasgow Health Board, strongly disagreed. 'It's very difficult to say with such apparently arrogant confidence that spending is too high. It's a bit like saying you are spending too much on immunisation because there

are so few cases of polio or whooping cough.'

Dr Gruer points to the low levels of HIV infection among drug abusers in Scotland compared to Europe as evidence that the health education programme is working, and he says that funds are being focused on gay men and those travelling to areas of high risk.

Dr Andrew Tannahill, general manager of the Health Education Board for Scotland, said: 'People mustn't drop their guard against Aids. The epidemic is still growing and Scots are becoming infected with HIV through heterosexual sex as well as sharing needles and homosexual sex.'

● About £32 million was spent on Aids prevention programmes in England and Wales in 1993. About £20 million was allocated to local health boards with £11.5 million going to the Health Education Authority. About 8,000 people have died of Aids in Britain in the last 12 years.

© *The Times*
August, 1995

Time to be angry

Linda Wilkinson wonders why scientists have not, as yet, found a cure for AIDS

My first brush with the virus which was subsequently to be known as HIV was in the early 80s, when I was running a haemophilia centre. Surmising (as it turned out, correctly) that the organism might affect haemophiliacs who received large amounts of plasma products, we tried in vain to get some sense out of the Centers for Disease Control in the United States. The only people who would communicate with us sensibly, however, were Gay Men Fighting AIDS in New York. The material which they sent displayed not only a willingness to help, but also an anger which by now must surely be of monumental proportions.

In the years since the discovery of HIV a vast amount of research time, money and effort have been spent on the disease. The primary objective was always to find a cure.

AZT, as we are all aware, was a previously-shelved drug which, although highly toxic, ameliorated the symptoms of infection. Taken up by the biomedical companies, this compound has spawned a whole family of other reverse transcriptase inhibitors which, together with anti-fungals and drugs to control secondary infection, have kept our pharmaceutical giants very buoyant on the stock market.

Yet the reality is far more complex. AZT and the like give rise to resistant viral strains which, combined with bone marrow suppression, render them virtually useless until end-stage disease. The long-yearned-for vaccines have not materialised, and a cure seems like a glimmering jewel which remains tantalisingly out of reach.

Why, given all of the intellectual power invested in HIV research, can't we crack the nut, find the golden bullet?

A core of scientists working on HIV acknowledge that there simply hasn't been enough time spent on understanding the basic disease – that, in the all-too-understandable rush to find a cure, they may have missed seeing the wood for looking at the trees.

> ### Why, given all of the intellectual power invested in HIV research, can't we crack the nut, find the golden bullet?

A recent flurry of arguments in the scientific press show that even some of the more established players in HIV research know they may be up a blind alley. There are alternative theories as to the action of HIV and how it functions – theories which, if proven, would answer many of the paradoxes surrounding the infection and its resistance to treatment.

Most of these ideas are, however, 'hypothesis driven', not tested, because the scientists can't get the funding to do the work. None of us likes to see money thrown away inappropriately. Yet it seems that is exactly what is happening in our persistence in going down the same old alley, applying the same old tenets and dogmas about a very clever organism.

HIV infection, so we are told, is a disease of immunodeficiency, a disease in which the body succumbs to a plethora of organisms attacking a defenceless host. Not so! There is indisputable evidence that until the end-stage disease, the body is in a state of immune activation. This idea of overreaction is no myth and its acceptance would fundamentally alter the way in which we treat the disease.

Indeed, contained in that very flurry of scientific frustration was a plea to look back, not in anger, but to learn – for as far back as 1988, reports of the similarity of HIV infection to the autoimmune

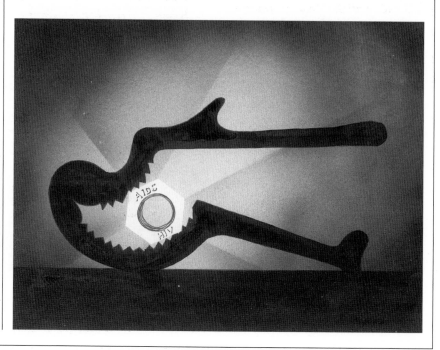

(immune activation) diseases were published. The continuation of this research has received little public funding, nor has it been part of the commercial sector's search for a cure, yet the evidence which has emerged answers many of the paradoxes surrounding the action of HIV. Autoimmune diseases are a group of disorders in which the body turns against itself, most classically in response to a bone marrow transplant. This is not the place to go into scientific theory, but suffice it to say that part of the HIV coating, the part which binds to CD4, is very like part of the body's own defences. It is not irrational to suppose that the body, recognising this substance as similar but not self, might set up a reaction. If the substance is more like 'self' then the disease progresses more slowly, if less similar, more quickly. This would also explain part of the genetic basis to disease resistance.

The next series of drugs to be released into the HIV market-place, the protease inhibitors, primarily inhibit HIV maturation. Yet, given the experience with AZT, one wonders how long before resistant strains will arise and we are back to square one. For it seems pointless to base treatment on viral replication alone when it's obvious that the whole virus, coating as well, may play a major part in the disease process.

So, back to angry. I am. Angry at the prejudice and lack of vision which has left us without an end in sight. Angry at a society complacent in its white, Western, heterosexuality. Angry for my scientific colleagues fighting, from a very tight corner, for what they believe to be right and just.

The tide may be about to turn but we must nurture it, watch it carefully, and yes, yet again, be more than a little angry until the battle is won.

● Linda Wilkinson is a former University College, London, research worker and is now a freelance writer and researcher in the field of autoimmunity and arthritis.

Stab in the dark

Edward King asks whether safer-sex campaigns are working

New research published this week suggests that there has been no reduction in the annual HIV-infection rate among gay men over the last six years. How are AIDS educators going to react to this depressing news? Does it mean that safer-sex campaigns aren't working?

The new figures were published in the *British Medical Journal*. Researchers looked at the results from four laboratories which perform HIV antibody tests for genito-urinary clinics in London. To make sure that they were analysing recent infections, they looked at gay men who tested HIV negative at some point after January 1988 but at a later test had become infected.

Of these 1,759 repeat testers, 124 had become infected with HIV by April 1994. The annual risk of becoming infected was highest for men aged 20 to 24, at 6.2%.

When the researchers looked at only the men who had become infected within two years of their last negative test, the annual infection rate was 9% for men aged under 30, and 3.3% for older men.

There was no evidence that this risk had decreased at all between 1988 and 1994.

It is highly unlikely that a single campaign, particularly one that relies on printed materials, will have a dramatic effect on sexual behaviour

---

These figures aren't without their limitations. They only represent infection rates among a sub-group of gay men who have taken more than one test at GUM clinics in London, and some researchers have doubts about the statistical methods used. But if they're right, don't they show that recent safer-sex campaigns have failed to make an impact?

You could try to argue that a stable infection rate over six years is a good result, because the alternative is that it could have gone up. After all, each year there are more people with HIV who could potentially infect others. It's always impossible to come up with theories for why things could have been made much worse, but most people will probably argue that infection rates as high as these should cause concern.

Many AIDS organisations will probably shrug off the figures as saying nothing about the effectiveness of their education campaigns. Up to a point they're right, because, as Graham Hart, a sociologist with the Medical Research Council, points out: 'Infection rates are not a sensitive way of measuring the effects of a specific intervention.'

There are two main reasons why it's foolish to expect a particular leaflet or poster campaign to make a noticeable impression on the HIV statistics. The first is that it is highly unlikely that a single campaign, particularly one that relies on printed materials, will have a dramatic effect on sexual behaviour.

Secondly, in a setting where there are so many factors that could impact on decisions about safer sex, raw statistics don't let you tease out the factors that have most impact from those that do little or nothing.

Does this mean that AIDS educators have no way of knowing whether their work is doing any good? Worse still, can we tell if some campaigns are actually counter-productive, putting people off safer sex?

Graham Hart and a small umber of other researchers around the world are becoming increasingly concerned about these questions. They worry that it's become commonplace for AIDS groups to access the effects of their work only by measurements such as the number of condoms they distribute or the number of men they contact during an outreach session. Very few educators try to measure the effects of their work by, for example, assessing people's level of knowledge or even their sexual behaviour before the campaign, then investigating whether it has changed afterwards. As I've said, that may be impossibly hard in places like London, where gay men are exposed to so many different sources of information and influence about HIV. But it could well be feasible in smaller cities with more stable populations and fewer distractions.

Even if the new figures can't tell us anything about the effectiveness of particular projects in London, they do suggest that safer-sex efforts taken as a whole aren't having the impact that AIDS groups should be aiming for. Taking into account the full range of factors that might influence people's sexual behaviour – not only formal campaigns and materials from a range of organisations, but also articles in the gay press and even the conversations we have with friends about sex and AIDS – it seems that the overall effect is still not good enough.

Over the past few years, those of us who have campaigned for the re-gaying of AIDS can justly claim that we've secured a much greater level of funding for gay men's safer-sex campaigns. Now that the fight for quantity has largely been won, it's high time we focused on quality. We need to confront the question of whether the money is being spent effectively on worthwhile campaigns that are helping to prevent new infections.

If not, the money might just as well be left in the health authorities' coffers, and the growing gay men's AIDS sector will amount to little more than jobs for the boys.

The origins of HIV

By Phyllida Brown

The first documented case of HIV infection dates back to 1959, in a sailor in Manchester, England, who died of what we now call AIDS. Tests of stored tissue from the man's body have shown clearly that he was infected with the virus, and he suffered classical symptoms of the disease. It is quite likely that a few people had AIDS even earlier. But scientists are convinced that it is new as a widespread disease.

No one knows how or when HIV first entered the human population, or where. There have been many bizarre theories about its origin: for example, some people have blamed it on the CIA in the US and claimed that it is an agent of biological warfare. But HIV does not need such outlandish explanations for its existence. HIV is related to other immunodeficiency viruses that infect other primates.

The most plausible theory is that it entered the human population at some point in the past, and then remained isolated in a small or isolated group who may not have been severely affected by it. Its explosive spread probably began only in the middle of this century when urbanisation, cheap travel and world wars made widespread travel common and vastly increased the potential for people from different communities to have sex with each other.

In fact, there are two known HIVs: HIV-1, which is found worldwide, and HIV-2, which was originally restricted to West Africa but is now appearing in Asia and Europe. HIV-2 is genetically similar to two species of simian immuno-deficiency virus (SIV) which infect macaques and sooty mangabeys. But HIV-1 is much less closely related to SIV. If HIV-1 and HIV-2 come from a single common ancestor, many years must have elapsed to enable them to diverge.

How did HIV 'jump' species? Early in the epidemic, a few armchair anthropologists caused massive offence by claiming – without the slightest evidence – that HIV had entered the human population when people had had sex with monkeys. Once again, we do not need such outlandish explanations. Many animal viruses have entered the human population in much less dramatic ways. In some communities, people eat monkeys, and in butchering a carcass it is quite possible that animal blood was splashed into someone's eye or into a cut, for example.

Another once-popular theory is the idea that HIV accidentally entered the human population through trials of early polio vaccines. The vaccine is grown in monkey kidney cells and in theory a fore-runner of HIV could have infected these cells. However, an expert panel of scientists have concluded that this can almost certainly be ruled out. For one thing, the timing is wrong: the Manchester seaman was probably already ill by the time some of the vaccination trials were under way.

Scientists in Aids breakthrough

'Most important results in decade of research'

Steve Connor
Science Correspondent

Scientists are claiming a breakthrough in the treatment of Aids based on the latest results of one of the world's largest clinical trials of anti-HIV drugs, involving thousands of patients.

A combination of two drugs taken over a period of more than two years led to a fall in death-rates of nearly 40 per cent. It is the first Aids drug trial to show a significant, long-term benefit in extending a patient's life expectancy.

Medical researchers conducting the effort, which involved 3,000 patients in eight European countries, claimed yesterday that the results were the most important to emerge in nearly a decade of research into Aids treatment.

Britain's Medical Research Council, which took a lead in the investigation, will announce the results today at a scientific meeting in Copenhagen. It has already recommended that Aids patients should begin taking a combination of at least two anti-HIV drugs.

The drugs in question are compounds known to interfere with the ability of HIV to replicate. One of them, AZT, made by the British company Wellcome, has been used since 1986 but was partially discredited as a single-drug therapy after it was shown in 1993 not to prevent healthy HIV-positive people from developing Aids.

However, the so-called Delta trial used AZT together with one of two other antiviral drugs – ddI and ddC, made respectively by Bristol Myers Squibb of the US and Roche of Switzerland. 'The reduction in death-rate over the course of the trial was 38 per cent for patients who took two drugs compared with those who took AZT alone,' the MRC said.

Brian Gazzard, clinical director of the Aids unit at the Chelsea and Westminster Hospital in London and the UK's main investigator on the Delta trial, said: 'It's the first trial to show an improvement in long-term survival of Aids patients.'

> **A combination of two drugs taken over a period of more than two years led to a fall in death-rates of nearly 40 per cent**

Although the trial does not resolve the issue of when is the best time to begin treatment – whether with healthy HIV-positive people or those showing signs of Aids – Dr Gazzard said the advantages of taking two drugs are clear: 'If you're thinking of starting treatment, you should start with combination therapy, not AZT alone.'

Dr Gazzard said it would cost between £3,000 and £5,000 a year to treat an Aids patient with two antiviral drugs.

The best improvements in survival occurred in patients who had not previously taken AZT by itself. The Medical Research Council said it was 'too early to say whether or not those who have already taken AZT may benefit from combination therapy'.

Nevertheless, patients on the trial taking AZT alone have now been offered the chance of having it in combination with ddI or ddC because scientists considered it unethical to continue single-drug treatment in the light of the Delta results.

Tim Peto, a consultant in infectious diseases at the John Radcliffe Hospital in Oxford, said yesterday that the research is the most significant in anti-Aids drugs since 1986, when it was found that AZT gave a short-term benefit for Aids patients. 'We're not trying to say "this is it", we're saying it's a significant clinical advance,' he said.

Nick Partridge, chief executive of the Terrence Higgins Trust, an Aids charity, said the Delta results were 'good news' after two years of disappointments and setbacks. 'Although we are a long way from a cure, these results renew hope, improve current treatment and encourage researchers looking at other combinations of drugs.'

Mr Partridge stressed that the trial does not provide all the answers. 'While these drug combinations can slow progression to Aids they do not prevent it and the increase in life expectancy is still quite small. Delta does not clarify when to start treatment, how long to take the drugs, or which combination is most effective,' he said.

The continuing story

Continuum magazine tackles issues of positive living and works against the prevalent notion that HIV is the cause of AIDS. Here it adds its voice to Positive Times' coverage of the HIV debate last month

Continuum is one of several local organisations challenging the theory that HIV is the cause of AIDS, and internationally that number grows to dozens. This is a brief introduction to the arguments underpinning our views.

1 AIDS isn't a single disease – it's a syndrome collection of diseases, all of which can occur in the absence of HIV.

2 Some 39% of AIDS-defining illnesses have never been demonstrated to depend on a prior immune suppression, including KS, lymphoma, dementia, cachexia (wasting) and diarrhoea.

3 Most people who are HIV positive do not have AIDS, and over 4,000 clinical diagnoses of AIDS have been made in 'HIV antibody' negative people.

4 The definition of AIDS in Africa is radically different from that in the West, so the two conditions cannot be considered the same.

5 The common ELISA and Western Blot antibody (AIDS) tests can give positive results if a person has antibodies associated with MS, generalised warts, hep B (or vaccine), Epstein Barr virus (glandular fever), malaria, leprosy and some flu vaccines.

6 Antibodies are proof that a person's body has made an immune response against a foreign agent; 'HIV antibodies' are the first to be used to infer the opposite, therefore a vaccine is impossible.

7 It is theorised that HIV infects T-cells and kills them, yet 'HIV' has been grown in lab cultures of T-cells since 1984.

8 T-cell counts are now routinely used to predict disease progression, yet they've never been demonstrated to be an accurate marker for this.

9 Unlike all other known viruses, HIV has not been isolated according to simple standard procedure.

10 Approximately 75% of the US haemophiliacs are 'HIV antibody' positive or have AIDS diagnoses, reportedly having caught the virus from the Factor VIII blood product that they used. The US Government agency responsible for AIDS – the CDC – confirmed last year that drying of blood products reduces the chance of infection to 'zero'. Factor VIII is freeze-dried and stored for long periods. Therefore, haemophiliacs could not be suffering from ill health due to HIV infection.

11 'The trouble is the side-effects of AZT are similar to AIDS symptoms,' says Prof Tony Pinching, respected AIDS immunologist. Continuum magazine readers are, on the whole, people who have stayed away from toxic medications. We find that both health and illness are multifactorial in nature. The power of a positive diagnosis can shock people into a fatal series of self-destructive choices.

There has never been any real evidence that AIDS is infectious, just as there has never been any real evidence that HIV causes AIDS, or that so-called HIV antibodies are specific to the virus.

● Continuum can be contacted by writing to: PO Box 2754 London NW10 8UF or by phoning 0181 961 1170.

Photo: Jacky Chapman / Format

The definition of AIDS in Africa is radically different from that in the West

HIV virus does cause AIDS, research shows

By Sharon Kingman

A study of the death-rates among patients with haemophilia in Britain between 1977 and 1992 provides clear evidence that the human immunodeficiency virus causes AIDS. Researchers in Oxford, writing in the 7 September issue of *Nature*, show that the large increase in deaths of patients with haemophilia since the mid-1980s is due entirely to HIV. Dr Sarah Darby of the Imperial Cancer Research Fund Cancer Epidemiology Unit in Oxford says that the effects of HIV infection on deaths among patients with haemophilia have been 'specific and enormous'. She says that the study 'strongly contradicts the suggestions that HIV does not cause AIDS. It shows very clearly that HIV can cause AIDS, and that HIV can cause death, and that the risks are very big.'

Dr Darby and her colleagues looked at the deaths of all patients on the UK National Haemophilia Register between 1977 and 1992. A total of 1227 of the 6278 men diagnosed with haemophilia and living in Britain were infected with HIV between 1979 and 1986 as a result of receiving contaminated blood products. The estimated median time of seroconversion was late 1982.

Among 2448 men who had severe haemophilia the annual death-rate remained stable at 8 per 1000 between 1977 and 1984. Between 1985 and 1992 the death-rate stayed at 8 per 1000 among patients who were HIV negative, but rose steeply for the group of 1020 patients who were HIV positive, reaching a rate of 81 per 1000 in 1991-2.

A similar pattern was seen for 3830 patients with mild or moderate haemophilia, who received fewer treatments with blood products and were therefore at lower risk of HIV infection. Among this group the death-rate was 4 per 1000 in 1977-84, but it rose to 85 per 1000 in 1991-2 among a group of 207 patients who were HIV positive.

Between 1985 and 1992 there were 403 deaths among patients with haemophilia who were HIV positive; only 60 would have been expected from the death-rate in non infected patients. Dr Paul Giangrande of the Oxford Haemophilia Centre, another author of the paper, says that this suggests that 85% of these deaths were due to HIV. He says,

'We found that the overall increase in the death-rate is entirely accounted for by a very large rise in deaths among HIV-positive patients. The rate in uninfected patients is unchanged.' The deaths were mainly due to AIDS or to conditions known to be associated with AIDS.

Dr Darby says, 'These are the first data to document that, in a large and complete population, deaths among those who by chance were infected by HIV were more than ten times higher than deaths among those who escaped infection. The increase applies regardless of the severity of the haemophilia.'

© *British Medical Journal*
9 September, 1995

It is a fact that . . .

- Already 14 million people are infected with HIV worldwide.
- By the year 2000 between 30 and 40 million people will be infected with HIV globally.
- 1 in 250 of the world's adult population are already infected.
- You cannot tell by outward appearance who has HIV.
- Every 15 seconds someone is infected with HIV – the virus causing AIDS.
- 50% of people infected with HIV will become ill within 10 years, many of the rest after 15 years.
- Sexually transmitted diseases and the number of sexual partners increase the risk of HIV infection.
- There is no cure or vaccine for AIDS.
- HIV is spreading at an increasing rate in almost every country. No community or country can claim that they have been able to stop this spread.
- Many people with HIV don't become ill for a long time and may not know that they are carrying the virus.
- In the UK around 8,000 people have developed AIDS and approximately 30,000 are infected with HIV.
- Even though someone with HIV may feel well for many years they are still able to pass on the virus.

- The above is an extract from *HIV Facts for life*, published by ACET. See page 39 for address details.

HIV, pregnancy and children

Plain speaking about HIV and AIDS and how it affects women, written for women by the experts – women

Your child and your rights

If you or your child are antibody positive, you mustn't worry that the child will be taken into care by the council's social services department. Social workers have a clearly defined brief and that's to give support to parents and children AT HOME. Your child cannot be taken away and put into care simply because the parents or the child have HIV infection or AIDS. There is also no reason your children will be taken into care if you are claiming Attendance or Mobility Allowance.

If you have any problems over housing, benefits or legal rights, call Positively Women and we will put you in touch with experts who can give you professional and confidential advice.

HIV infection and AIDS are becoming a problem when children are abused sexually and when women are raped. If this has happened to you or your child, do not agree to an HIV test without getting fully informed about the test and before you're given proper counselling. If your test turns out to be positive, contact Positively Women.

Pregnancy

If you're antibody positive to HIV, should you get pregnant? Opinions differ, but the facts as we have them are:

- All babies born to HIV antibody positive mothers are born with their mother's positive maternal antibodies.
- After 6 to 18 months the maternal antibodies clear and research suggests that approximately 70-87% of babies will be virus-free (though these statistics are constantly changing). Obviously, that means that 13-30% of babies will have HIV infection and these children are at risk of developing AIDS.
- The most common way for a baby to become infected with HIV is in the womb or during birth. HIV-positive women who have good access to milk formula (soya formula suits some babies better) and sterile feeding equipment and water are advised not to breast-feed as it can increase the chances of transmitting the virus.

A lot of doctors advise women who are antibody positive to HIV to have a termination. Armed with the facts given above, a woman must be left to make up her own mind. If she decides

POSITIVELY WOMEN

to go ahead with the pregnancy she should be given all the support she needs. If you're in this situation, we advise you to call Positively Women straight away.

If you're already pregnant, make sure your antenatal clinic doesn't test your blood for HIV antibodies without your fully informed consent. You have the right to refuse. When they're taking your blood for the usual tests, ask what tests are going to be done. If you consent to an HIV antibody test, make sure you get full counselling before the test and after the result. If your test comes back positive, call Positively Women.

If you decide to go ahead with a termination, don't feel guilty about it. Remember, it's your choice.

If you or your partner are HIV antibody positive and you're thinking seriously about having a baby, there are several things you should think about:

- There's the risk of your getting infected if you're negative and your partner's positive.
- If you're positive and your partner is negative, you run the risk of infecting him.
- If you are both positive you may run the risk of re-exposure to the virus. People have asked if, when both partners are positive, there is a higher chance of the child being infected. This is not the case – the risk does not change.

Artificial insemination

When one partner is HIV positive, some couples decide to opt for artificial insemination by donor – thus not putting the negative partner at risk through unsafe sex. Many women who are not in a relationship with a man also choose artificial insemination. Remember, donated sperm may also contain HIV– so it's advisable to contact a reputable agency like the British Pregnancy Advisory Service, which screens all donors for HIV, if you are considering this method of getting pregnant.

Birth

In the past there has been conflicting information, but the general consensus now is that whether you choose vaginal or Caesarean delivery, the risk of infection is the same. Everyone should be treated the same in hospital regardless of their status but unfortunately this is not always the case. Extra precautions are sometimes taken when a woman has been honest enough to reveal her HIV status. Until attitudes change, those of us who are positive will always encounter a certain amount of ignorance.

There is now some evidence that the longer the period between the membrane rupturing and birth, the greater the chances of transmission. If a woman already has a child who is HIV+ the chances of subsequent children being infected at birth are increased.

Children who are antibody positive

Like adults, children can be infected and remain completely well.

In the early stages, children who are positive may suffer from ordinary childhood conditions – such as diarrhoea, running nose, sore throat or ears, skin rashes, kidney problems and lung disorders. Other possible difficulties include slow development, lack of coordination and seizures. All of these can be early symptoms of HIV infection.

More severe symptoms of HIV infection can be serious lung problems – which may need long-term treatment with oxygen, and cancers, such as lymphoma of the central nervous system.

If your child is antibody positive to HIV and shows any of the symptoms we have listed here, see your doctor. The condition could be a minor childhood ailment; it's often very difficult to tell the difference.

But if it is HIV-related, prompt treatment could avoid problems in the future.

The Department of Health recommends that all positive children, whether symptomatic or not, should be immunised against measles, mumps and rubella. They should also be immunised against polio and whooping cough, using an inactivated vaccine. It is important to remember that if your child has been given a live polio vaccination, any member of your family who has AIDS may be at risk as the polio virus may be excreted in urine; so be careful, for example, when changing nappies. BCG vaccinations should NOT be given. For further information consult your doctor.

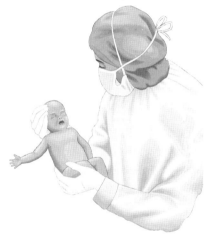

If your child comes into contact with chickenpox or measles, even if they have been immunised, you should contact your GP as soon as possible, as they may need a shot of immunoglobulin in case they have not developed sufficient antibodies to cope with these infections.

Children who are antibody negative

Many HIV antibody positive women may find it difficult to have a loving relationship with their children who are antibody negative. They don't need to worry. It's impossible to infect a child through loving and affectionate behaviour.

You may find yourself becoming a bit neurotic over this. If you do, call Positively Women – more often than not we can help, as many of us are positive mothers ourselves.

Make sure you carry out standard hygienic practices: cover any open sores, cuts or grazes with a plaster.

Living in the community

If, for some reason, you decide to tell your neighbours that you, or your child, have HIV infection, think about it carefully before you go ahead.

A lot of people are still ill-informed. If you feel you have to tell the neighbours, gauge their reaction by talking about HIV infection in a general sense.

If they are obviously ignorant about the subject, slowly try to educate them yourself. Once you have done all this you may decide to go ahead and tell them about your, or your child's, antibody status.

You'll want to keep your life as stress-free as possible. If telling them is going to cause you any aggravation, don't say a word. If you have to tell them, get someone who knows about HIV to be present to support you.

If it's you who has got HIV infection, think about what happens to your child if you fall ill. The obvious thing to do is to arrange support through your immediate family or close friends. For your own peace of mind make sure you've made a will, saying exactly who's going to care for your child. If you don't have any family or friends you can fully rely on, see the bit about foster parents further down this page.

If it's your child who's got HIV infection, it's important to allow them to play freely with other children in the community. There are no known cases of children infecting each other through everyday activities.

Most local authorities have very clear policies on what help and support parents or children who have HIV infection need.

If coping at home is difficult, ask your local authority for a home help.

Day nurseries and day care facilities should always accept a child with HIV infection – so should registered child-minders. Everyone involved should have had full training from the local authority, not just in looking after children with HIV infection but also in counteracting discrimination.

If you can't take full care of your own child, the local authority should ensure that any foster parents are fully briefed on the care and support a child who has HIV infection needs.

Schools

Children who have HIV infection should attend school freely. Parents whose children are antibody positive to HIV need not tell the school authorities, although you may find it preferable to inform the head teacher, to make sure your child gets full support. Ask the head to give you an assurance the school's staff won't write or talk about it as confidentiality is imperative.

There is no record of HIV being transmitted at school – if this were the case, thousands of children would be infected.

Children who have HIV infection are entitled to receive as normal an education as possible and to be allowed access to the full range of school activities – and it's not just us who say so, that is a quote from the Local Authority Associations' Officer Working Group on AIDS.

Your child shouldn't be stigmatised at school and shouldn't be hassled by the other children or their parents. Bear that in mind when you're deciding what you tell the school – and who you inform.

Positively Women

An organisation run by women for women with HIV and AIDS. We offer the following services: support groups, open only to women who have HIV and AIDS, telephone and one-to-one counselling and consultancy services. Write to us at 5 Sebastian Street, London EC1V 0HE or phone us on 0171 490 5515.

Positively Women produces other leaflets in the series *Women and AIDS*, including the following:

1 *Prevention*
2 *Positive Result?*
3 *HIV, Pregnancy and Children*
4 *Women, Drugs and HIV*

and a booklet – *African Women's Health Issues*

● Copies of these publications can be obtained from Positively Women. See page 39 for address details.

AIDS: *the children's tragedy*

'A decade ago, women and children seemed to be on the periphery of the AIDS epidemic. Today, women and children are *at the centre of our concern.*'

Worldwide, as many women as men are contracting the AIDS virus. In Africa, women now account for 55% of all new cases of HIV.

As the AIDS epidemic grows, it is becoming clear that women are more vulnerable than men. The reasons are both biological and social. Biologically, women are at more risk because a larger mucosal surface is exposed during sexual intercourse and because semen carries a greater concentration of the virus than vaginal fluid. Socially, they are more vulnerable because they tend to marry or have sex with older men who have had more sexual partners and because they may have little or no choice about whether and with whom they have sex. Often, women are not in a position either to say no or to influence their partner's sexual behaviour (including whether or not condoms are used).

In some areas of Africa, 25% to 30% of pregnant women attending antenatal clinics are HIV positive. One in three of their babies will be born with the virus. All will develop AIDS and most will die before the age of five. So far, approximately 1 million children have been infected and half a million have already died – almost all of them in Africa.

HIV is also known to have been transmitted by breast milk in some instances. But breast-feeding is still recommended in areas where the risk from malnutrition and disease is paramount.

Two-thirds of all new cases of HIV are now occurring in Africa, where 9 million children will be orphaned in the 1990s and where recent gains in child survival are being reversed. In Zimbabwe, for example, AIDS has already become the biggest single killer of the nation's under-fives.

But the situation in some countries in Asia is giving almost as much cause for concern. Thailand reports that 1 adult in 50 is infected with HIV, and a study by Mahidol University suggests that the country's under-five mortality rate will rise by 10% before the end of the century.

With no AIDS vaccine in sight, only behavioural change offers hope of altering the course of an epidemic that could see 26 million people infected and an annual death toll of almost 2 million by the year 2000. Sex education for young people (60% of new HIV infections occur in the 15-to-24 age group) is essential. And recent studies have strengthened this case by showing that sex education is not associated with either more or earlier sexual activity.

Even more fundamentally, the growing AIDS threat to women and children will not diminish until women have more power to say no to sex, to choose their own partners, and to influence sexual behaviour.

Resources are also required. Yet, of the estimated $2 billion spent annually on AIDS prevention, only about 10% is spent in the developing world, where 85% of infections are occurring.

● The above is an extract from *The State of the World's Children*, published by UNICEF.

Report says 3,000 children face death of their mothers to virus

By Liz Hunt
Medical Correspondent

More than 3,000 children in the UK have mothers infected with the Aids virus, and face a childhood blighted by caring for a sick parent likely to die before they reach their teens. About 2,000 are aged 10 or under.

A report by Barnado's provides the first UK estimate of the numbers of children with HIV-positive mothers. Overall, the number is set to increase by one-third in the next two years, and will continue rising after that.

The majority of affected children live in Greater London and, of those, more than 1,200 are under 10. Many are from Black and ethnic minority communities with parents who are African-born or are recent immigrants or asylum seekers in Britain.

There are more than 600 children in Scotland (350 under 10), which was the area initially hardest hit by the heterosexual spread of HIV among injecting drug users. The authors said their report does not include fathers who are HIV positive as data on them is not available.

The report found that children of HIV-positive mothers were more likely to be poor, homeless or living in run-down accommodation. Older children were often responsible for caring for their sick parents and younger siblings. Many did not have English as their first language.

All the children were routinely affected by upheavals in their homelife when their mother was sick or had to be admitted to hospital. Their education was also badly disrupted.

'Ultimately, they are likely to face the trauma of the death of one or more of their parents,' according to John Imrie, a health promotion researcher at the London School of Hygiene and Tropical Medicine, and one of the report's authors.

Mike Jarman, director of Barnardo's Child Care, said yesterday that most HIV services had been set up for adults and there was a worrying gap in the services for children. He said: 'It is the children of parents with Aids who will be greatly in need of support and care for many years

> *Overall, the number is set to increase by one-third in the next two years, and will continue rising after that*

ahead. There are still not enough of the right kind of services which meet children's particular needs.' Barnado's is calling for more practical help to be offered to affected families, including respite care, domestic help, maximisation of benefits, and regular breaks for parents and children. 'The aim is to reduce stress and create an environment where future arrangements for the children can be discussed with confidence,' a spokeswoman for Barnado's said. The report also urges more research into circumstances of HIV-affected children to better target limited resources.

● The report *No Time to Waste* is available from Barnado's Child Care Publications, Tanners Lane, Barkingside, Ilford, Essex IG6 lQG, price £8.50.

© The Independent
June, 1995

Go-ahead for baboon cell AIDS hope

By Roger Highfield, Science Editor

A risky treatment for AIDS, in which baboon bone marrow is injected into patients, has been given the go-ahead by the US Food and Drug Administration.

The Aids virus, HIV, attacks the production in the marrow of white blood cells which fight infection.

The scientists reason that if the immune system of a sufferer were supplemented with marrow cells from baboons, which appear impervious to the virus, the patient may be able to overcome the infection.

An FDA advisory committee said last month that the operation would probably kill recipients, already in the last stages of the disease. But a spokesman said: 'These people have no alternative.'

© The Telegraph plc
August, 1995

Does AIDS affect children?

Many children and young people around the world have been affected by AIDS. Lives are threatened, communities changed and hopes dashed. For some, childhood will not even be a memory.

Practise what you preach is a commonly held belief. But in the serious business of saving young people's lives, it has got to be 'preach what you practise'. To combat the ever-increasing crisis, education needs to be credible, and delivered by believable people. HIV/AIDS education in the UK and worldwide has often fallen short of adequacy.

Sex education in schools has always been a controversial area. Many believe it is vital, while others believe it encourages sexual activity among the young. There is, however, increasing proof that, far from promoting early sexual activity, good sex education actually causes young people to delay embarking on sexual relationships.

Since 1988, ACET has been teaching in schools and colleges in the UK and worldwide. This type of education is essential for HIV/AIDS prevention. There are some concerning trends regarding the sexual practices of our young people today. It is known, for example, that teenage pregnancies are on the increase. We are also aware that sexually transmitted diseases are increasing among young people and a National Survey of Sexual Attitudes and Lifestyles (1992) revealed a rising pattern of sexual activity in the under-25s.

Teenagers today are the AIDS generation. With 1 in 250 of the entire adult population already infected, and with one new person being infected every 15 seconds, this is not a problem which will go away.

The battle for our young people's hearts, minds, souls and bodies does not start or end in the classroom. Youngsters absorb life around them, learning through each of their senses. To reach and teach young people we must see home, community and family strengthened in their effectiveness. We must ensure that young people are given a choice between life and death. We all have a responsibility. Whether we are teachers, governors, parents, brothers, sisters, church or community leaders, we must ensure that we, as the messengers of life, reflect the message in the way we practise, as well in what we preach.

Children have already been affected. For many there is no turning back. Our hope at ACET is that we can support those already in need with practical care and help in the long-term battle by educating where the need is greatest.

The future lies in the hands of those who are children now. . .we have a huge responsibility to inform them of the truth.

● The above is an extract from an *ACET Newsletter*. © *ACET*

World AIDS cases reach one million

The number of people in the world known to have AIDS is now officially over one million. The World Health Organisation estimated in January 1995 that the real figure is about 4.5 million, due to incomplete reporting and under-diagnosis. This represents a rise of 20% in AIDS cases since January 1994. A total of 19.5 million have been infected by the HIV virus since the pandemic began in the late 1970s, including 1.5 million children.

A report in *The Times* on 1st January 1995 stated, 'The condition could afflict 40 million people by the end of the decade.'

It is figures such as these that make many people realise that HIV/AIDS has not gone away, nor will it.

● The above is an extract from an *ACET Newsletter*. © *ACET*

No time to waste

The scale and dimensions of the problem of children affected by HIV/AIDS in the UK. By John Imrie and Yolande Coombes

A summary

An increasing number of children in the UK live with a parent who is HIV-infected or who has AIDS. Also, an increasing number of children and young people have been orphaned by the death of one or both parents from an HIV/AIDS-related illness.

The vast majority of these children are not *infected* with HIV. However, as No Time to Waste demonstrates, they are seriously *affected* by HIV[1] in a variety of ways. *No Time to Waste* focuses on four key areas: the number of children affected by HIV; the circumstances of children affected by HIV; the needs of children affected by HIV and current provision for meeting those needs; recommendations for developing appropriate services

How many children in the UK are affected by HIV?

Information on the numbers of children affected by HIV in the UK is not routinely collected. This report is the first attempt to estimate the number of affected children in this country, using a statistical demographic model.

The report makes the following estimates for the UK:
- there are currently over 3000 HIV-affected children
- over 2000 children under 10 are affected by HIV

There is considerable variation in the geographical spread of affected children:
- there are over 1800 affected children in the Thames region
- there are over 600 affected children living in Scotland, concentrated in Edinburgh and Lothian region, Greater Glasgow, and Dundee

Only publicly available data were used to arrive at these estimates. Beginning from the reported number of women infected with HIV, estimates were made of the number of children likely to have been born to these women (based on age-specific fertility data for women born in the

Estimated numbers and age distribution of HIV-affected children

In the United Kingdom, 1991, 1993, 1995 and 1997*

Year	<5 years	5-9 years	10-14 years	15-18 years	Estimated annual total < 18 years	> 18 years	Estimated cumulative total
1991	938.5	863.9	569.7	278.3	2650.4	294.3	2945.0
1993	882.4	929.1	687.7	345.5	3844.7	423.0	3267.7
1995	*987.4*	*1038.88*	*768.47*	*385.95*	*3180.7*	*472.47*	*3653.18*
1997	*1092.42*	*1148.66*	*849.23*	*426.40*	*3516.7*	*521.95*	*4038.66*

* All figures printed in italics indicate projected values

By geographical area in the United Kingdom in 1995

Region	<5 years	5-9 years	10-14 years	15-18 years	Estimated annual total < 18 years	> 18 years	Estimated cumulative total
Thames Regions	619.6	610.0	425.3	206.7	1861.5	249.7	2111.2
Rest of England, Wales and Northern Ireland	203.3	229.2	178.1	98.8	709.5	140.7	850.2
Scotland	164.5	199.7	165.1	80.5	609.7	82.0	691.8

UK). There is no available data on the number of children a father has (regardless of HIV infection) or the numbers of HIV-infected fathers. It has therefore not been possible to incorporate HIV-infected fathers into the model.

These figures therefore offer an incomplete picture and are likely to be conservative underestimates. Nevertheless, they provide a useful indication of the substantial number of children requiring services.

The circumstances of HIV-affected children, their families and communities:

- Most affected children in the UK are under age 10 and live with a biological parent.
- A significant proportion of HIV-affected children are children of injecting drug users, or of gay or bisexual fathers.
- A large proportion of HIV-affected children in the Thames region are from Black and ethnic minority communities and many of these have parents who are African-born, and/or recent immigrants or asylum seekers in this country.

HIV-affected children are more likely than the general population to be disadvantaged in a number of ways:

- HIV-affected children are more likely to live in sub-standard housing or be homeless and are more likely to be poor.
- HIV-affected children are more likely to suffer educational disadvantages (many children do not have English as a first language), or may suffer from a range of behavioural problems.
- HIV-affected children are often responsible for caring for sick parents and siblings.

- For many families, the deteriorating health of the principal income earner leads to a severe reduction in the family's standard of living, with associated stresses and complications.

The needs of HIV-affected children and current provision for services

The needs of HIV-affected children are distinct from the needs of their parents and families. Ten areas of need are identified in the report:

- Welfare rights and financial provisions
- Housing and transport
- Education and information
- Legal issues
- Care and support
- Mental health
- Recreation and respite
- Transitional support
- Bereavement and grieving
- Confidentiality

The Children Act gives guidance, financial provisions and clear policy intentions which can assist agencies in meeting the needs of HIV-affected children. The UN Convention of the Rights of the Child (which the UK Government has signed) sets out the need to consider the particular needs of children. In addition, this research consistently points to the need for children to be more involved in identifying needs and developing services to meet them.

Barnardo's recommendations

The recommendations arising from the report include the following points:

1 Children affected by HIV have distinct needs, which differ from those experienced by children affected by other life-limiting illnesses The unpredictable career of HIV infection and the social stigma frequently attached make them a particularly vulnerable group.
2 HIV-affected children are not a homogenous group. Agencies providing services to children need to plan for children of all ages.
3 All agencies providing services to HIV-positive people have responsibility for ensuring, in consultation with clients, that the needs of children are considered.
4 Top priority should be attached to the provision of practical help to affected families. Respite care, domestic help at home, maximisation of benefits, and breaks for both children and parents are all likely to decrease immediate stress and to create an environment where the future arrangements for the care of children can be discussed with less stress and more confidence.

The report also concludes that current knowledge and understanding of the situation of HIV-affected children in the UK is patchy. Far more is needed in this area in the way of both collection of data and research.

- The full report, *No Time to Waste*, is available from Barnardo's Child Care Publications, Barnardo's Trading Estate, Paycocke Road, Basildon, Essex SS14 3DP; tel 01268 520224; price £8.50.

[1] HIV here refers to the spectrum of HIV disease, including infection and AIDS.
© *Barnardo's*

Hope for HIV babies as boy 'loses' virus

By Celia Hall
Medical Editor

A baby in America tested HIV positive after birth but found to be clear of the virus a year later may provide proof that babies born to HIV mothers can rid themselves of the virus.

The boy, now five and still HIV negative, is not the first case to show this phenomenon, but his case is the best documented. Others have been dismissed as laboratory mistakes.

The researchers from the UCLA School of Medicine, Los Angeles, say in the *New England Journal of Medicine* that their results indicate that HIV clearance can happen and may have been under-recognised.

Dr Marie-Louise Newell, co-ordinator of the European collaborative study of children born to HIV mothers, which is currently monitoring 1,800 cases, said: 'This might help in pointing the way for vaccine research or confirm that research is moving in the right direction.

'What needs to happen now is investigation of the child's immune system to see if anything can be found to explain what happened.

'There have been a number of cases like this in children from Europe but people have been a bit sceptical of the results. A great deal of work was done on this case and it is nicely documented, reliable data.'

Dr Newell, an epidemiologist at the Institute of Child Health in London, pointed out that levels of the virus in the baby had been very low.

The boy's mother was tested positive for HIV during pregnancy. The baby was found to have the virus when he was tested 19 days after birth and again at 51 days old. At a year old, he had a routine test and was found to be negative. Numerous, sophisticated tests since to find the virus have failed. Reports exist of virus resistance in adults. A group of Gambian prostitutes have remained uninfected despite long exposure to HIV, and sexual partners of known HIV cases have also remained clear.

The American findings raise more questions than they answer. The researchers say it is still possible that the boy has a 'hidden' virus which could re-emerge at a later date.

> **'There have been a number of cases like this in children from Europe but people have been a bit sceptical of the results'**

In an accompanying commentary in the journal, Dr Kenneth McKintosh, of Boston Children's Hospital, says the findings are hard to explain. He says: 'Does this mean that in a proportion of infants HIV in some form enters the foetus or the new-born and is then cleared?' He said it would be surprising if it was found that there was an effective immunological response in babies as the immune systems in new-borns are considered to be immature.

Dr McKintosh says that in the light of the new case it seems that previous, less well studied cases, which had been dismissed, perhaps 'were not errors, at least not all of them'.

Gaz Daly, spokesman for the charity Aids Care Education and Training, said: 'Obviously it is very good to hear this news, but one has to treat it with caution. The difficulty here is that many people who have HIV and want children may be tempted to go ahead.

'They must accept that a baby could be infected and that they only have five or six years to live.'

© *The Independent*
March, 1995

Aids – the HIV test

Yes or no? This information is for anyone who is thinking of having a blood test called the HIV antibody test. It tells you all about the test and explains what the results mean. It also raises some of the points you might want to think about before you decide whether to have the test.

What is AIDS?

AIDS stands for Acquired Immune Deficiency Syndrome. AIDS is caused by a virus called HIV (Human Immunodeficiency Virus). The virus can damage the body's defence system so that it cannot fight certain infections and other diseases.

HIV cannot be passed on through everyday contact.

HIV can be passed from one person to another in three main ways:

- through unprotected sex (anal or vaginal);
- by sharing drug injecting equipment;
- from an infected mother to her baby before or during birth, or by breast-feeding.

You cannot pass on the virus by kissing, cuddling, shaking hands, sharing cups, plates, knives and forks, or by using the same toilet or bath. You cannot catch HIV in the same way as colds or flu or by being in the same room as someone with the virus.

In the past, some people got HIV through infected blood or blood products. This may still happen in some areas of the world. But it is very unlikely in most developed countries, including the UK. Here all blood donations have been screened and blood plasma products specially treated since October 1985.

Some people have HIV for many years without having any symptoms or illness. Many may not know they are infected. Some people may be quite unwell due to the virus while others may have less severe illness.

There is at present no cure for HIV infection itself. However, much research is being done to find a cure. Many of the infections you might get when you have HIV can now be treated.

What is the test?

When people become infected with HIV, they produce antibodies to the virus. The test looks for these antibodies in their blood.

It is not a test for AIDS. It will only tell if you have been infected by the virus. It will not tell you if you have AIDS, and cannot predict when you might go on to develop AIDS.

What does the test involve?

A doctor or nurse will take a sample of blood, usually from your arm. They will then send it to a laboratory for the HIV antibody test. Your result and the fact you have been tested are confidential between you, the doctor and other staff directly concerned with your care.

It may take about two weeks before you get your result. Some clinics can give you the result the same day. Clinics will only give *you* your result, so you have to go back in person. You cannot get your result over the phone.

What does the result tell you?

Negative result

A negative result means that antibodies to HIV have not been found in your blood. This means that you most likely have not been infected with the virus. However, it can take up to three months after infection, and sometimes longer, before antibodies show up in a blood test.

If you think you may have been infected then seek advice. But you may be asked to wait at least three months before having the test.

A negative result does not mean that you are immune to HIV. You can still get infected in the future if you put yourself at risk.

Positive result

A positive result means that antibodies to HIV have been found in your blood. This means that infection with HIV has occurred. (This may not be so for new-born babies of infected mothers who test positive. Tests on babies at this age show only the mother's antibodies.)

A positive result does *not* mean you have AIDS. It does mean that you have HIV and you can pass it on to other people:

- through unprotected sex;
- by sharing injecting equipment;
- a woman with HIV can pass the virus on to her baby before or during birth, or by breast-feeding.

If you have HIV you cannot infect someone by everyday contact. Drinking, eating, working or sharing a house with other people are all safe. You can be as close and loving with your own or other people's children.

Where to get a test

Contact a clinic anywhere in the UK. Some clinics go by different names. Look in the phone book under:

- Genito-urinary medicine (GUM) clinic
- Sexually transmitted disease (STD) clinic
- Venereal disease (VD) clinic.

You can get a test through your GP or at an HIV testing clinic. Pregnant women can ask for a test at their antenatal clinic.

Private clinics offer the test but will charge a fee. Not all offer

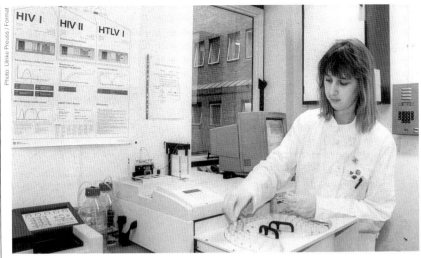

Photo: Ulrike Preuss / Format

follow-up care and advice. They can refer you on to an NHS clinic if you wish.

Talking it over

Talk to a health adviser or doctor at the clinic or to your GP before you decide whether to have the test. They will help you think through the issues of having it.

Think carefully about who else you might choose to discuss it with. Ask yourself, who else really needs to know and why? It may be hard to keep the result confidential if you tell friends you are having the test. They will most likely want to know the result. Employers and work colleagues do not need to know you are thinking of having the test, let alone what the result is.

If you are not sure where to go or who to talk to, the National AIDS Helpline on 0800 567 123 will be able to advise you and discuss the issues of having a test. Calls are free, confidential and lines are open 24 hours a day. Calls will not appear itemised on phone bills.

There are phonelines in other languages too and for those with hearing difficulties (listed at the end of this article).

Should I have the test?

Only you can decide. Allow plenty of time to think about the issues. Here are some points to consider:

Making changes

Knowing whether you have HIV may help you in making choices about your lifestyle, your job, your sex life or your family's future.

Having children

Taking the test may help you decide whether to have children or carry on with a pregnancy.

Serious illness

If you need treatment for serious illness it is vital for your doctor to diagnose your condition. Infections you might get if you have HIV can be treated – the earlier the better.

Some people can react badly if they learn that you have HIV. There are now many groups that can help to support you in dealing with this.

Your job may be put at risk if it becomes known that you have the virus. There is no law to prevent an employer refusing to employ people with HIV. However, many employers now have rules stopping discrimination against people because of HIV.

Be aware that if you apply for life assurance or a mortgage, your doctor may be asked to provide information about your medical history, including details of an HIV antibody test.

Here are some other questions to consider:

- Am I likely to be infected? Have you placed yourself at risk through unprotected sex or by sharing injecting equipment? Remember, HIV cannot be passed on by everyday contact, including kissing.
- Are other people at risk? Do you think you may have unknowingly passed on the virus to someone else? They may need to be told if your result is positive. They may wish to consider taking the test. They may also want to take steps to avoid passing on HIV. You may be concerned about how they might react to the news. Health advisers can offer you help.

How can I protect myself and others from HIV?

Here are some points to consider, whether or not you take the test:

Choose safer sex
Using a condom correctly every time can help protect you and your partner from the risk of HIV and other infections passed on during sex.

Use condoms with plenty of water-based lubricant (such as KY jelly). Do not use oil-based lubricants (such as Vaseline or baby oil). These will damage the rubber.

Ways of having sex that carry little or no risk of passing on the virus include: kissing, mutual masturbation, rubbing your body against your partner's and massage.

Don't share injecting drug equipment
If you do inject drugs don't share 'works'. Always use your own equipment. Never lend or borrow syringes, needles, spoons, bowls or water. Needle-exchange schemes offer supplies of clean equipment and will safely dispose of used equipment. For more details about needle exchange contact your local drug service or call the National AIDS Helpline on 0800 567 123 or the National Drugs Helpline on 0800 776600.

You may feel you have no choice but to share. You can reduce the risk of infection by cleaning your works. Cleaning may help. But it is never as safe as using your own or new works.

Clean used works
in the following way
1 Draw cold water into the syringe. Then flush it out. Sterile or cooled boiled water is best. Do this twice.

2 Draw some household bleach or diluted washing-up liquid into the syringe. Then flush it out. Do this twice as well.

3 Finally flush the syringe out twice with fresh water.

Cold water on its own is not enough to make sure it is clean. Always use bleach or washing-up liquid as well.

Make sure the needle goes all the way into the liquid. Flush the liquid into a separate container or down the sink or toilet.

If you want to talk about the test, or any other aspect of HIV or AIDS with a trained adviser, you can contact one at a clinic. You can also call the National AIDS Helpline on 0800 567 123. Calls are free, confidential and lines are open 24 hours a day, 7 days a week. Calls will not appear on itemised phone bills.

Phonelines in other languages:
- Welsh 0800 371 131 from 10am-2am daily.
- Bengali 0800 371 132 from 6pm-10pm Tuesdays.
- Punjabi 0800 371 133 from 6pm-10pm Wednesdays.
- Gujarati 0800 371 134 from 6pm-10pm Wednesdays.
- Urdu 0800 371 135 from 6pm-10pm Wednesdays.
- Hindi 0800 371 136 from 6pm-10pm Wednesdays.
- Arabic 0800 282 447 from 6pm-10pm Thursdays.
- Cantonese 0800 282 446 from 6pm-10pm Mondays.
- A Minicom Service is available for people with hearing difficulties. Lines are open on 0800 521 361 from 10am-10pm daily.

Call the National AIDS Helpline for free copies of this or other leaflets about HIV.
- *The facts about HIV and AIDS*
- *Your guide to safer sex and the condom.*

© *Health Education Authority*
November, 1995

HIV and Aids in the United Kingdom

In the UK, 1,789 new cases of AIDS were reported in 1994, an increase of 11 % on the previous year. This brought the total since the start of the epidemic to 10,304, of whom 7,019 are known to have died.

The total number of reports of HIV infection from the beginning of the epidemic to the end of December 1994 is 23,104, of which 2,411 were reported in 1994. Of the infections reported since the start of the epidemic, 60% were transmitted by sexual intercourse between men, and 17% transmitted by sexual intercourse between men and women. In England, Wales and Northern Ireland the largest number of transmissions occurred through sex between men. In Scotland, injecting drug use is the largest single exposure category, accounting for nearly half of all infections.

Source: Communicable Disease Report published by the Public Health Laboratory Service, 1995 no 3.

Home testing raises hackles

Julian Meldrum asks: should pharmacists be allowed to sell home testing kits for HIV?

Johnson and Johnson, famous for such domestic products as Baby Oil, has filed an application to the US Food and Drug Administration to market 'home testing kits' for HIV antibodies.

The package the company is offering would go well beyond mere reagents. They have promised special hotlines with trained counsellors to explain results and a free mail-in confirmatory testing service, so that no one should have to rely on the one test – an essential precaution, in view of the false positive rates which are reported even with the best of tests used by trained laboratory staff.

The company argues that there is public demand for such tests, which may have a variety of uses, including helping people to make better-informed decisions about whether to have unprotected sex in relationships and encouraging prompt access to treatments of proven value in limiting illness and disability among people who are HIV positive.

Furthermore, they argue that there is such pressure on anonymous testing services in many parts of the United States that it is common for people to receive their results by phone, and that their proposed package could be something of an improvement on existing services in some cases.

More controversially, the company is reported to be offering substantial financial support to the magazine *Poz*, which has adverts featuring glowing HIV-positive models endorsing a variety of products for people living with HIV and AIDS.

While a decision is awaited from the US FDA, in the UK the Department of Health issued regulations in 1992 banning the direct sale of home HIV-testing kits to the public, although recent experience of trying to get action taken against a small-time entrepreneur making an effort to do precisely that – and without any of the back-up promised by US companies – raises questions about who is responsible for enforcing such regulations, and what their status might be.

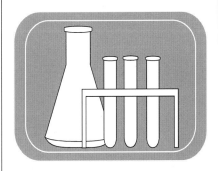

Tests could be administered for non-medical reasons, such as by prospective employers

On the one hand, Department of Health guidance to health authorities has encouraged expanded access to HIV testing at a wider range of locations. 'Same day' testing clinics have multiplied since they were pioneered by the Royal Free Hospital in London.

On the other hand, no one in the UK has argued that it is good practice to give HIV-test results by phone. And the idea of distributing packages based on existing blood or salivary antibody tests for home use raises further problems which make it very unlikely to win support in the field.

For example, the test could be used without consent on children or dependent adults, whose circumstances could be adversely affected by a false result. Or tests could be administered for non-medical reasons, such as by prospective employers, without the safeguard of a requirement for the involvement of medical personnel accountable to their professional bodies.

People might be drawn to use home tests precisely because their fear of HIV and AIDS made them afraid to approach specialist services. On testing positive they might still feel unable to approach such services and, in extreme cases, act in destructive or self-destructive ways.

What of the partners of HIV-positive individuals who test negative on 'salivary' tests because they fail to follow the instructions precisely enough? They might have good cause to complain – and perhaps take legal action.

It would only take a few such cases to discredit those who were selling or promoting the tests concerned.

For all of these and other reasons, NAT and other HIV agencies have opposed the selling of home testing kits for HIV. But are we being paternalistic and – for example – preventing gay men who are well informed about HIV and who wish to pursue a strategy of 'negotiated safety' from doing so in a realistic way? At what point does the public, or a section of it, become sufficiently well educated for the issues to change? When, and on what basis, should we change our minds?

This article is based in part on information received via POS+NET from the US Centers for Disease Control National AIDS Clearinghouse.

● The above is an extract from *AIDSMatters*, No. 18. *AIDSMatters* is edited by Julian Meldrum and published free of charge.

AIDS and HIV infection

A guide for adults – from AVERT

What worries do people have?

Many people, in the course of their work and leisure, have occasions when they are concerned about possible exposure to HIV. Sometimes people find used needles and syringes in parks, the street or other public places.

Some people need to administer first aid. People who give blood may feel concerned about whether their blood is being tested for HIV. Some people may even feel concerns about the contact they have with doctors, dentists and nurses in which blood is involved.

Am I at risk from needles and syringes in the street?

If you discover needles and syringes anywhere you should not touch them. If you have children you might want to stress this point with them. In fact, the chances are very small of any HIV surviving for any length of time in blood in a syringe or on a needle. But other infections like hepatitis and septicaemia can definitely result from getting pricked with dirty injecting equipment.

What about the risks in giving first aid?

People who take first aid courses should, as part of their training, be told how to deal with risks of infection. There are also some simple things that anybody dealing with even minor cuts and injuries can do. Always wear rubber or plastic gloves, and cover any existing cuts and grazes you might have with waterproof dressings.

After administering first aid, use plenty of disinfectant and soapy water if you are clearing up blood or other body fluids, and continue to wear gloves. If you can, dispose of any blood or vomit in a toilet. If you have to administer mouth-to-mouth resuscitation you should, whenever possible, use a mouth-piece from a first aid kit.

AIDS & HIV

The figures

The first person with AIDS in the UK was diagnosed in 1981. By 1995 over 11,000 people in the UK had been diagnosed as having AIDS. Nearly three-quarters of these people have already died.

It is much harder to say how many people are infected with HIV. By 1995 over 24,000 people were known to be infected. Of these, about:
20,500 are men
3,200 are women
600 are children

But these are only the people who are known to be infected. The actual number of infected people could be five times greater. This means that the number of men, women and children infected in the UK could already be over 100,000.

The facts
- Every day the number of people infected with HIV in the UK increases.
- There is no cure for AIDS.
- We all need to act now to reduce the effect that HIV infection and AIDS will have in the future.

© AVERT

Am I at risk if I give blood?

Will they tell me if there is a problem?

There is no risk of infection to people who give blood in the UK. All the equipment used is sterile and is only used once. When someone donates blood it is tested for a range of infections including HIV.

If there is any infection present the donor will be contacted and a meeting arranged to discuss what has been found. Results are never given over the phone or by letter.

If you receive donated blood in the UK there is almost no risk of HIV infection, because since 1985 all donated blood has been tested for HIV.

Are there risks in seeing a dentist or doctor or nurse?

No. There are no recorded instances in the UK of any patients being infected with HIV by medical staff.

What should I do if I think I might have been at risk?

If you think you may have been exposed to any blood-borne infection you should think seriously about seeking medical advice.

If the risk was through a cut or a graze contacting someone else's blood, or if it was through an accidental prick with a dirty needle you should pinch the cut or puncture to make it bleed. Then wash it thoroughly with soap and water and cover it with a plaster.

If you are at work you should always report any injury, however minor.

So what are the general rules about reducing the risk of HIV infection?

Everyone should be wearing protective gloves and being careful when dealing with blood and body fluids – whenever they come into contact with anybody who is bleeding or who needs first aid.

Nowadays most medical staff have a policy called universal precautions. This means taking precautions with everybody. If precautions are taken with everyone then no judgements have to be made about who might have an infection.

Whenever you hear about HIV you know someone's going to mention condoms. Does everybody really need to be concerned about sexual risk?

Worldwide, most people with HIV have become infected by having sexual intercourse with a person of the opposite sex. Sexual risk is very important to consider because the virus can pass quite easily between people in semen and vaginal secretions.

Condoms are mentioned so often in connection with HIV because using a condom makes it very hard for the virus to pass between people when they are having sex.

Of course, sex is an embarrassing subject and some people have strong moral feelings about talking about sex at all. It can be even more difficult to consider talking to young people in particular about condoms and sex. But the sometimes notorious stories about young people, their sex education and their sexual behaviour may distract people from having to think about adults.

Many adults have several serious sexual relationships in the course of their lives. Some people find their marriages and long-term relationships breaking up and find themselves seeking new partners. All these people need to consider, as much as young people, if they are at any risk of HIV, or placing their new partner at risk.

Anybody embarking on a new sexual relationship ought to consider practising 'safer sex', for example using male or female condoms if you are having sexual intercourse. Perhaps this article could be part of talking to a new partner about HIV and this issue.

● The above is an extract from *AIDS and HIV infection – a guide for adults*, produced by AVERT. See page 39 for address details.

Aids study offers fresh hope

*By Roger Highfield,
Science Editor*

Scientists have discovered the first evidence in humans that protection against HIV is possible. Their research has important implications for the development of an Aids vaccine.

Harvard Aids Institute researchers report today in the journal *Science* that infection with the second, milder, Aids virus – HIV-2 – sharply reduces the chance of becoming infected with HIV-1, the virus causing the Aids epidemic.

'Since HIV-2 can lead to Aids and death, we are not suggesting using it as a live vaccine,' said Dr Phyllis Kanki.

'These findings suggest a new avenue for research into fine-tuning the natural protection and delivering it in the form of a safe vaccine.'

In the study of 756 women licensed as commercial sex workers in Dakar, Senegal, from 1985 to 1994, researchers found infection with HIV-2 reduced the women's chances of acquiring HIV-1 infection by about 70 per cent.

This occurred despite a higher incidence of gonorrhoea, which suggests that HIV-2 infected women had not cut their exposure to HIV-1 through a change in their behaviour.

'This study suggests we ought to look at HIV-2 more carefully,' said Dr Kanki. 'Clearly HIV-2 is triggering a resistance response that in some way protects against HIV-1 infection. The next step will be to study the women in greater detail to learn precisely how this immunity is manifested.'

Dr Max Essex, co-author, said: 'A vaccine that mimics the immunologic response to HIV-2 infection may offer a high degree of protection against HIV-1. 'This work shows it may be possible to induce immunity to protect against very different strains of HIV.'

Ideally, researchers say, a vaccine could stimulate an immune response similar to that triggered by HIV-2 but not expose patients to the risk of HIV-2 infection.

This might be accomplished by using components of HIV-2 that mimic natural infection with the whole virus.

Related yet distinct viruses have been successfully used to vaccinate against other diseases in animals and humans.

The cowpox virus, for example, was used to generate the first vaccine and ultimately to eradicate small pox.

The study has yielded other findings, including the initial identification of HIV-2, which has been confined primarily to West Africa. Research has shown that rates of disease development are slower in people with HIV-2 than those with HIV-1 – observations that led to the idea that the weaker virus might protect against HIV-1.

Facing the challenge of HIV and AIDS

From The Terrence Higgins Trust

HIV and AIDS affect us all. What are we doing for you?

The Terrence Higgins Trust is here to help anybody affected by HIV and AIDS. Our work falls into three main areas: we offer counselling, advice, support and practical help to anyone who calls on us; we take preventative education to as many people as possible to stop further infection; and we campaign on behalf of all those discriminated against by their HIV status. The HIV virus can affect anybody at any time. Although some sections of the community have been particularly affected – enduring unimaginable losses – the virus seems now to be spreading most quickly within the heterosexual population. For every person infected with the virus, there may be a partner, a lover, a mother, a father, children, friends, work colleagues who are all about to discover, in varying degrees, what it's like living with AIDS.

Carrying on the fight

HIV and AIDS has been with us for more than a decade and right from the start the Trust has been at the forefront of the fight.

We have watched the virus spread and witnessed the affect on those it has infected. The latest research indicates that people are living with AIDS for a lot longer than originally thought, which means the Trust is going to be needed for a long time to come. We intend to be around for as long as is necessary.

Stopping the spread of HIV

The Trust doesn't judge people but tries to persuade them to take as much care of their health as possible. Our Health Promotion campaigns communicate the importance of practising safer sex and safer drug use, with hard-hitting posters, leaflets, videos and postcards. Fund-raising events raise awareness and communicate our work to a massive audience. Making sure we get our message across to every section of society is crucial if we are to protect both present and future generations.

Facing the challenge of AIDS requires that we know as much about the virus as possible. The Trust's Library hosts one of the largest collection of information on HIV and AIDS in Europe. It is as valuable to people with a positive diagnosis as it is to nurses, health workers, teachers and the general public – all of whom want to find out as much as they can about the virus.

Someone to talk to

If you are worried or need advice and someone to talk to, you can ring The Terrence Higgins Trust any day of the year. Our Helpline is staffed by trained volunteers from 12 noon until 10 pm. They can discuss your worries with you and offer support; give advice on safer sex; talk you through the pros and cons of taking an HIV test; tell you where to get a test if you decide to take one and put you in touch with our counsellors should you receive a positive diagnosis. Through our Counselling Service you can arrange face-to-face counselling sessions in complete confidence. Our resident trained counsellors are skilled in helping people find a way of handling the many emotional and practical aspects of living with HIV and AIDS. You can arrange to be seen individually, with your partner or in a family, for a maximum of 12 one-hour sessions. Our Advice Centre can offer expert advice on a broad range of issues such as welfare, housing and legal matters.

Friends in deed

When someone is diagnosed HIV positive, they may find their friends are unable to cope with the emotional strain of the situation. The Trust's pioneering Buddy Scheme offers people with AIDS who live in the Greater London area someone they can rely on when friends and Social Services are not enough. A Buddy is a specially trained volunteer who can give whatever practical help is

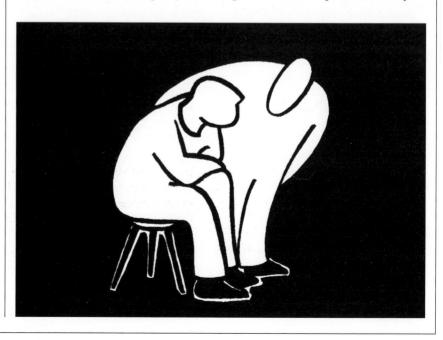

needed, from sorting out bills, mowing the grass, making supper ... to just plain listening. Above all, they are someone to be there when they're needed.

Positive help

Coping with the practicalities of everyday life can be difficult when you are living with AIDS. The Trust tries to offer as much practical help as possible. The Small Grants Fund gives financial support to those who are unable to work because of illness and may not have sufficient funds to pay for the special diet or treatments they need. The Fund is able to make one-off donations to pay an outstanding bill or make a gift of something such as a washing-machine – essential for someone coping with night sweats. The Helper Cell is a unit of over 150 volunteers who are ready to carry out many practical tasks, from driving someone to hospital to plumbing in a shower. They also offer an interpreting service with volunteers speaking more than 15 languages – easing communication with hospital staff or Social Services. The Terrence Higgins Trust Advice Centre offers assistance with all manner of legal, housing and welfare problems. Many people with a positive diagnosis are currently suffering the iniquities of the system. They may not be receiving all the benefits they are entitled to, may be living in unsuitable accommodation or may have been unfairly dismissed from work because of their HIV status. The Trust has qualified lawyers and experts in the benefit and housing systems who are able to fight on your behalf against such discrimination.

Half the fight is ignorance

Part of the battle against HIV and AIDS is overcoming people's prejudice and ignorance. The Terrence Higgins Trust lobbies Parliament on all issues relating to HIV and fights for those who have been discriminated against on the grounds of HIV in the workplace. Recent successes include reducing, with other pressure groups, the age of consent for gay men to 18 years. We shall continue to lobby for a further reduction, as the present law makes it very difficult

for the Trust to promote safer sex to young gay men. After a five-year campaign the Trust's Insurance Working Party has successfully lobbied for a change in the questions to be answered on life insurance forms. Now applicants are no longer required to state whether or not they have been tested HIV negative. Previously even a negative test could result in an increased premium.

How The Terrence Higgins Trust began

Terrence Higgins died with AIDS in 1982, knowing very little of the virus that had taken over his body. The lack of support and information that was available to him shocked and upset his family and friends. They determined that no one else should suffer such indignity again and decided to found an organisation in his name. Today the Trust is the UK's leading AIDS service organisation, channelling the efforts of over 1,300 volunteers. Anyone, regardless of age, race or gender, can call on us at any time, whether for themselves or on behalf of a relative or friend.

Together we can face the challenge

The Trust was born out of the generosity of the human spirit. It is that same spirit we are appealing to

now. After you have read about all we are achieving you may be saddened to learn we are being forced to cut essential services due to lack of funds.

And this at a time when what we really need to be doing is increasing the amount of help we can offer people. The severe reduction in our Government grant has meant we are more than ever reliant on the generosity of individuals. By making a donation to the Trust you will be helping us maintain services, which in many instances are not available anywhere else, but are greatly relied upon by a growing number of people. Whatever amount you can send to the Trust will make a very real difference to our work. Living with HIV and AIDS is a big enough challenge in itself, even with all the help the Trust can offer. Please do not stand by and watch our good work slowly being eroded, simply from lack of funds. Thank you for whatever amount you can spare.

● The above is from a leaflet called *Facing the challenge of HIV and AIDS*, produced by The Terrence Higgins Trust. See page 39 for address details.

© *The Terrence Higgins Trust 1995*

Protection for HIV victims

By Sarah Bosley

Sufferers from HIV are to be protected from discrimination at work under the Disability Bill which is due to become law by the end of the year. The bill, in which campaigners have already forced many changes, will be amended at its third reading this autumn.

It will specifically include sufferers from symptomatic HIV – those who have not yet developed AIDS – in a list of those with progressive illnesses who will enjoy the protection of the law.

In its current form, the Disability Discrimination Bill mentions as examples cancer, muscular dystrophy and multiple sclerosis. A spokesman for the Department of Social Security said yesterday that it always had been the Government's intention to include symptomatic HIV but it had recently decided to name it in an amendment rather than spell it out in secondary regulations after the bill has passed to the law.

© *The Guardian August, 1995*

INDEX

ADDITIONAL RESOURCES

You might like to contact the following organisations for further information. Due to the increasing cost of postage, many organisations cannot respond to enquiries unless they receive a stamped, addressed envelope.

Aids and Housing Project
Livingstone House
11 Carteret Street
London SW1H 9DL
Tel: 0171 222 6933
Encourages the development and management of good quality housing and accommodation for people living with HIV. Produces publications.

Aids Care, Education and Training (ACET)
PO Box 3693
London SW15 2BQ
Tel: 0181 780 0400
Fax: 0181 780 0450
Provides practical home care to people with Aids through a team of doctors, nurses and volunteers. Provides training courses and produces publications.

AIDS Education and Research Trust (AVERT)
11 Denne Parade
Horsham
West Sussex RH12 1JD
Tel: 01403 210202
Fax: 01403 211001
Works to prevent people becoming infected with HIV and dying from Aids, through education and research. Publishes a wide range of educational booklets. Ask for their Resources Catalogue.

AIDS Helpline (Northern Ireland)
Freephone 0800 326 117
Provides a wide range of services throughout Northern Ireland. Phone: Monday & Wednesday: 7.30pm – 10pm, Tuesday and Thursday: 10am – 1pm, Saturday: 2 – 5pm

Blackliners
Eurolink Centre
49 Effra Road
London SW2 1BZ
Tel: 0171 738 5274
Information on HIV targeted towards Black and Asian communities.

British Medical Association Foundation for AIDS
BMA House
Tavistock Square
London WC1H 9JP
Tel: 0171 383 6345
Fax: 0171 388 2544
Provides an information and advice service for anyone with a professional interest in HIV and AIDS. Produces publications.

CAB International
Wallingford
Oxon OX10
Tel: 01491 832 111
Fax: 01491 833 508
Publishes *AIDS Newsletter* and, *Current AIDS Literature* and recently on CD-ROM, *CAB Health*, a compilation of current journal articles, book extracts and conference papers.

Health Education Authority
Health Promotion Information Centre
Hamilton House
Mabledon Place
London WC1H 9TX
Tel: 0171 413 1995
Publishes a wide range of free HIV and AIDS-related booklets.

Health Information Service
Health Publications Unit
Manchester Road
Heywood, Lancs
Freephone 0800 665544
Provides a range of information on health services including the NHS, self-help groups and complementary therapies.

National AIDS Helpline
Freephone: 0800 567 123
Distributes a free range of information sheets.

National AIDS Trust
6th Floor, Eileen House
80 Newington Causeway
London SE1 6EF
Tel: 0171 972 2845
Fax: 0171 972 2885

Voluntary organisation in the field of HIV and AIDS infection. Produces publications.

National Children's Bureau
8 Wakely Street
London EC1V 7QE
Tel: 0171 843 6000
Fax: 0171 278 9512
Provides information on children's needs in the family, school and society. They publish a series on fact sheets called Highlights. *HIV and Children* (Highlight No. 129) gives an overview of the current situation.

Oxfam
274 Banbury Road
Oxford OX2 7DZ
Tel: 01865 311 311
Produces a wide range of publication including free leaflets. Ask for their *Resources for Schools and Youth Workers* catalogue.

Positively Women
5 Sebastian Street
London EC1V 0HE
Tel: 0171 713 0222
Fax: 0171 490 1690
Provides free and strictly confidential practical and emotional support to women with HIV infection and AIDS. Produces publications.

Scottish AIDS Monitor
26 Anderson Place
Edinburgh EH6 5NP
Tel: 0131 555 4850
Provides a wide range of services throughout Scotland.

Terrence Higgins Trust
52-54 Gray's Inn Road
London WC1X 8JU
Tel: 0171 831 0330
Fax: 0171 242 0121
Promotes an understanding of HIV and AIDS issues by collecting and disseminating medical and social information. Publishes a wide range of free HIV and AIDS-related booklets.

ACKNOWLEDGEMENTS

The publisher is grateful for permission to reproduce the following material.

Chapter One: The current situation

Understanding HIV infection and AIDS, © The Terrence Higgins Trust, May 1995, *HIV/AIDS: a chronology,* © WorldAIDS, January 1995, *Social trends,* © HMSO Reproduced with the kind permission of Her Majesty's Stationery Office, 1995, *Exposure category of AIDS cases; cumulative totals to 31 December 1994,* © HMSO Reproduced with the kind permission of Her Majesty's Stationery Office, 1995, *Global statistics – AIDS,* © CAB International, *Understanding HIV infection and AIDS,* © The Terrence Higgins Trust, © May 1995, *Cumulative infections approach 20 million,* © WHO (GPA), 1995, *AIDS cases total passes 10,000,* © The Guardian, January 1995, *News from the Americas,* © WHO (GPA), 1995, *African villages cut HIV by 42 per cent,* © The Guardian, August 1995, *Africa is priority for new UN AIDS chief,* © WorldAIDS, March 1995, *A toehold,* © The Economist, August 1995, *Aids tide has turned in Europe, claims professor,* © The Sunday Telegraph plc, London 1995, *Aids epidemic 'threatens booming economies',* © The Guardian, September 1995, *The HIV bandits no prison can hold,* © The Daily Mail, July 1995, *Government is wasting funds on AIDS prevention,* © The Times, August 1995, *Time to be angry,* © The Pink Paper, August 1995, *Stab in the dark,* © The Pink Paper, September 1995, *Scientists in Aids breakthrough,* © The Independent, September 1995, *The continuing story,* © Positive Times, September 1995, *HIV virus does cause AIDS, research shows,* © The British Medical Journal, September 1995, *It is a fact that,* © ACET, 1994.

Chapter Two: The effects of HIV and AIDS

HIV, pregnancy and children, © Positively Women, 1995, *Report says 3,000 children face death of their mother to virus,* © The Independent, June 1995, *Go-ahead for baboon cell AIDS hope,* © The Telegraph plc, August 1995, *Does AIDS affect children?,* © ACET, *World AIDS cases reach one million,* © ACET, *No time to waste,* © Barnardo's, *Hope for HIV babies as boy 'loses' virus,* © The Independent, March 1995.

Chapter Three: Facing the threat

Aids – the HIV test, © Health Education Authority, *HIV and AIDS in the United Kingdom,* © Public Health Laboratory Service, 1995, *Home testing raises hackles,* © National AIDS Trust, February 1995, *AIDS and HIV infection,* © AVERT, September 1995, *AIDS & HIV,* © AVERT, September 1995, *AIDS study offers fresh hope,* © The Telegraph plc, *Facing the challenge of HIV and AIDS,* © The Terrence Higgins Trust, 1995, *Protection of HIV victims,* © The Guardian, August 1995.

Photographs and Illustrations

Page 2: Graphic News, pages 7, 26, 30, 36: Katherine Fleming / Folio Collective, pages 10, 20: Jacky Chapman / Format, pages 12, 28, 35: Andrew Smith / Folio Collective, page 15: Ken Pyne, page 16, 32: Anthony Haythornthwaite / Folio Collective, page 31: Ulrike Preuss / Format.

Craig Donnellan
Cambridge
January, 1996